THE EXPEDITION

Sir John organizes an expedition across an unknown continent. The recruitment of soldiers and native bearers, the voyage by sea and through virgin forest, difficulties due to sickness and desertion, the terror of attack from unseen enemies—all this is told in turn by Lieutenant Laronne and Sir John's interpreter Jaffar Topan. But Laronne and Jaffar seem never to see things in the same way, or to attach the same importance to events; they share only an utter indifference to the declared object of the expedition, which is to rescue a certain Kanyi Pasha. Even Sir John, a rigid disciplinarian who demands total loyalty of his companions, finds in the expedition merely a pretext for affirming the essential western virtues—pragmatism, solidarity, and the ability to organize.

This fable about European intervention in Africa makes structural and thematic use of Henry Morton Stanley's *In Darkest Africa*, the journal of his quest for and rescue of Emin, governor of Equatoria. But it is a use that is wholly modern. Unlike Stanley, the author does not profess to understand the motives behind the actions of his fellow-men; he merely observes, and records, and leaves the reader to draw his own conclusions.

PER OLOF SUNDMAN

THE EXPEDITION

TRANSLATED BY MARY SANDBACH

LONDON
SECKER & WARBURG

Published originally in Swedish under the title
EXPEDITIONEN
by P. A. Norstedt och Söner, Stockholm

English translation first published 1967 by
Martin Secker & Warburg Limited
14 Carlisle Street, London W.1

Printed in Great Britain by
Western Printing Services Ltd, Bristol

Above all circumnavigate Cape Bojador!

(Henry the Navigator's directions
to the men commanding his ships)

As we were starting, he stated his intention to die on the spot, called his countrymen together, distributed his bracelets, anklets, shiny iron collars and earrings among them, and then lay down with a placid countenance, wherein not the slightest emotion was discernible. All this was very admirable, but it would have been still more admirable to have bravely struggled, than to have so doggedly died.

(H. M. Stanley of a fellow traveller, a Mahdi chieftain,
who had trodden on a skewer planted in the ground)

Contents

Prefatory Note

In this book I have made considerable use of authentic material drawn from the writings of Henry Morton Stanley, particularly from his description of the expedition that lasted for almost three years: *In Darkest Africa: The Quest, Rescue and Retreat of Emin, Governor of Equatoria.* All the same my book is not about this relief expedition.

P.O.S.

Laronne

I

On one of our last days in Bari harbour we caught a thief, a boy, and it was Lieutenant Smitt in person who seized him.

The incident occurred on board the *Second*, just as they had finished loading her. The main part of our supplies were to be carried by the *Second*, whereas most of the expedition's askaris and pagazis were to be transported by the *Avanti*, our other ship. ('Askari' denotes soldier; by 'pagazi' we mean bearer or porter.)

The loading and stowage of the *Second* had occupied many days. The stores that Sir John had caused to be purchased lay piled up in two warehouses that he had rented from an English firm. With the help of his agent, the British Consul, the purchasing of these stores had begun long before we arrived in Bari. Our supplies were carried from the warehouses on board the *Second* partly by Barite porters, whom we had hired, and partly by casual labourers whom the Consul had put at our disposal. The distance between the warehouses and the ship was more than a thousand paces, and the bearers had to pass through a thick grove of palm trees and sugar-cane or rattan. What they were carrying were things they badly wanted, and we had to keep a sharp eye on them. I had posted a guard of Galla soldiers in the palm-grove.

So far as I know the only theft that took place was the one Lieutenant Smitt put a stop to.

As the loading was over and the warehouses empty I had gone down to the quay. It was a very hot afternoon and I was intending to seek some shade under the awning that was stretched over the *Second*'s quarter-deck. Just as I was going on board Lieutenant Smitt appeared from the ship's bows. He was holding the boy thief in a firm grip round his right wrist. He was laughing and having no difficulty in dragging his captive along. The boy was no more than a child, slight, emaciated by undernourishment, long-haired, and yelling shrilly.

Smitt came from the *Second*'s bows and walked aft. At first he was almost hidden by a mass of Barites who crowded round him like a swarm of bees. But the nearer he came to the stern the thinner grew the crowd: the stern of a ship is a place for Europeans.

'What's happened?' I asked.

Smitt laughed and pointed with his free hand.

'I've caught a thief,' he said. 'No more than a child, but he's already a thief.'

He went up to the table that had been placed at the edge of the shade cast by the awning, and by which the Barite porters had to pass with their burdens. Lieutenant Hansen, whose duty it was to enter up everything stowed on board the *Second*, was seated at this table.

'I happened to catch sight of him while he was still on the quay,' said Smitt. 'He was going to and fro, pattering about barefoot—he's all but naked anyhow—there he was pit-a-pattering about like a two-legged cat, his beady eyes peering out shiftily from under his mop of greasy hair, rather like a fleece it is. You can see for yourself there are plenty of people on the quay. Half Bari's collected there, isn't it? But my attention was drawn to him in particular. Then I suddenly noticed that he was sitting hunched up close to an open port-hole. You might almost have thought that he'd fallen asleep. He sat there for several hours.'

'What's he stolen?' I asked.

Smitt burst out laughing again.

'I don't know yet,' he said.

He twisted the boy's hand upwards and held it over Lieutenant Hansen's writing-table. This twisting movement forced the prisoner to his knees. He had stopped yelling. He had clenched his lips and his teeth; his dirt-encrusted fingers were tightly clenched too.

'It was when he sat down by the open port-hole pretending to be asleep that I really began to watch him in earnest,' said Lieutenant Smitt. 'I remembered that he'd been pattering to and fro alongside the ship.'

'What happened?' I asked.

'I drew back inboard, sir,' answered Smitt. 'I waited for perhaps a minute, and when I went back to the rail he'd disappeared. It seemed to me just possible that he'd made off towards the town, but I went down to the forehold, and that's where I found him. He tried to sneak out through the port-hole, but I grabbed hold of his leg and pulled him in again. Here he is. He doesn't weigh a lot. He's as thin as a squirrel and as slippery as an eel, but he didn't get away.'

The boy's right hand was tightly clenched.

'Open it,' said Lieutenant Smitt, trying in vain to force his thumb under the boy's finger-tips.

'He doesn't understand you, Lieutenant Smitt,' I said.

All round us, round Hansen's writing-table, a little group of Barites had gathered, ten, or perhaps twenty of them. They were probably pagazis whom Sir John had hired. The stevedores engaged by the British Consul would hardly have taken the liberty of collecting on the ship's quarter-deck.

The British Consul was an Irishman or a Scot with a long

and difficult name. When we spoke of him we called him Mac Effendi, the name by which he was generally known all over the island of Bari.

'What's he stolen?' asked Hansen.

Lieutenant Smitt began to laugh again. He seemed more delighted at catching a thief than interested in what that thief had stolen.

'Open your fist,' he said, passing his hand over the boy's head.

The boy's eyes were large and slightly protruding as if he were suffering from goitre or Graves's disease, though that seemed unlikely in view of his thin, slender neck.

'A child, but already a thief,' said Smitt. 'Come on, open your hand. How old are you? Twelve? Or ten?'

Lieutenant Hansen spoke:

'He doesn't understand what you're saying,' I said.

'We're used to our own children,' he said. 'I mean, our children grow up and develop and mature in quite another way. Things aren't the same here, among these Barites, are they? This is the first time I've visited Bari.'

It was at this point that Sir John arrived. He was followed by Dr Stre and Halmadi, the captain of our Barite soldiers.

Sir John asked what was going on and Smitt replied with a smile:

'I've caught a thief. But I don't yet know what he's stolen.'

Still holding him firmly with his left hand Smitt playfully scratched the boy's neck with the nails of his other hand.

'Let's see what you've got,' he said, in a friendly way, giving him a shove with his foot.

The young Barite was really very thin. You could count the ribs under his skin. His knees and elbows were thicker than his thighs and his upper arms, and his stomach was distended in a way said to be characteristic of those who, because of want and hunger, have eaten unsuitable food.

The hand in Smitt's grasp rested on Hansen's table. Sir John touched it with his cane and then twisted the boy's face upwards. His gaze was fixed and stony, his lips sucked in between his teeth.

Sitting at Hansen's table there was a scribe, a native of Bari. On our roll he was called 'moonshee', which is an Indian word meaning scribe. He was also employed as dragoman, because of his knowledge of languages.

This man bent across the table and spoke to the boy, who then burst into tears and opened his hand. A score or so of white pearls fell on to the table. The scribe gathered them up and gave them to me.

'No more than a child and already a fully fledged thief,' said Smitt.

The Barite boy got to his feet and Lieutenant Smitt let go his hold.

II

The young thief was taken ashore by two askaris. I do not know whether these soldiers belonged to us or to the Sultan of Bari. They led or carried the boy across the quay and we lost sight of them shortly before they turned off up one of the alleyways of the town.

Lieutenant Smitt watched them go; he seemed bewildered and he was no longer laughing.

I held the pearls in my hand; there were twenty at the most. I gave them to Sir John, who in his turn gave them to Hansen.

Smitt asked:

'Where are they taking the boy?'

Sir John's scribe said:

'The pearls were not beautiful. They lacked lustre, they were not quite round and the holes had been bored without care.'

'What will they do with him?' asked Lieutenant Smitt.

'I don't know,' replied Sir John. 'We're in Bari harbour and Bari has its own laws.'

'It was I who caught him.'

'You've already told us that, Lieutenant Smitt.'

'We've got back what was stolen, sir.'

'Lieutenant Smitt, stolen goods remain stolen even after they have been recovered,' answered Sir John.

His scribe said:

'Before the days of the Prophet thieves were condemned to death. They are less severe now. I am not a Muslim though I may seem to be one. They say that Allah punishes those He wishes to punish and forgives those He wishes to forgive. They chop off the hands of male and female thieves, effendim.'

Our medical man, Dr Stre, pointed out that the same law applied on board a ship as in its country of origin, at any rate when she was at sea. The *Avanti* and the *Second* belonged to a German firm. The *Avanti*'s captain was Dutch, the *Second*'s Scandinavian. To what extent were they familiar with German law?

For that matter, he said, was not the legal position further confused by the fact that the ships were chartered by us? Moreover—from the purely practical point of view—who would have acted as judge?

'We ought to have let him go,' said Lieutenant Smitt.

'That would certainly have been the simplest thing to do,' answered Sir John.

Jaffar Topan

I was in a deep sleep, Sayyid Bey woke me.

'What is it?' I said, half in my sleep.

I sat up, my head was heavy, my clothes sticky with sleep.

'What is it, effem?' I asked.

Sayyid gave me a beaker of water.

This water was a gift. I have never seen Sayyid Bey give anything to anyone. I have never seen him stretch out his arm with so much as a beaker of water to anyone but me.

The water was warm to drink. It cooled me when I splashed it over my face and breast.

I got up. The room had a door that opened on to a little balcony. The sun was low and the walls of the palace gleamed brightly.

Sayyid Bey sat down where I had just been sleeping. He was very fat and his breathing was laboured. He bent down to reach the mouthpiece of my pipe and took hold of it with his plump fingers. He really was very fat.

Bari had become a city because it had a harbour. The harbour was circular because a long, narrow tongue of land stretched out to protect it from the ocean. The tongue of land was half-moon shaped, like the emblem on a flag. The sun was low and there was no wind. I could see many boats and their sails hung limp.

'Are you awake now?' asked Sayyid Bey.

'I am awake,' I answered.

'I must talk to you,' he said.

'I must listen to what you have to say, effem,' I answered.

I went down on my knees and filled and lighted my pipe for him.

In the palace of the Sultan of Bari things are lit with European matches. The flame of a burning match is almost as broad as it is long. The flame itself is yellow. It seems to hover above the stick and in between there is a dividing patch of darkness. This dark patch, which sometimes appears to be blue, must really be part of the flame, for you cannot see through it.

The matches are made of some soft kind of wood. They are shiny. Grease has been pressed into them, tallow, lard or palm-oil.

Sayyid Bey was the first-born of the Sultan's twenty-eight sons, the eldest of an innumerable host of brothers and sisters.

The Barites know all there is to know about fathers and sons. They have little regard for mothers and daughters.

'Has the sun set?' he asked.

'Not yet,' I answered.

He went on smoking my pipe, sitting quite still. His eyes were almost closed and his cheeks drooped heavily over the bones of his lower jaw.

'The evening is drawing on, but it is not yet night,' I said.

'Is it not growing dark?'

'Not yet,' I said. 'Soon, effem! The sun is nearing the water, but you cannot yet look upon it.'

Sayyid, the Sultan's first-born, was already old. Rich and powerful men soon grow old. Yet there is a riddle here:

despite the fact that they age so early they live longer than those who lack riches and power.

Sayyid was very fat. He spoke slowly and he avoided unnecessary movement. Fat men listen in another way than thin men.

'How long has Mac Effendi lived here in Bari?' he asked.

'Always,' I answered.

'I can remember when he did not live here,' said Sayyid Bey. 'When was it that he did not live here in Bari? It was long ago. He has red hair and there are not many red-haired people. Jaffar, how low has the sun sunk?'

'For me he has always been here,' I said.

'What do you know about the small Englishman?'

'Is he small, effem?'

'Can you see his two ships?'

'They are moored in the harbour.'

'Can you see them?'

'They are hidden,' I answered. 'Mac Effendi is red-haired, but is the new Englishman small? The sun is lower now than it was a little while ago.

'For me Mac Effendi has always been here,' I said. 'He was here when I first stepped ashore. Don't you remember, effem? I fell over.'

'Did you fall?' said Sayyid Bey.

'I fell because I could only take short steps,' I said. 'I fell all the more heavily because I was compelled to hold my hands behind my back.'

'I do not remember, Jaffar.'

I lit my pipe for him again. He blew out thin clouds of smoke through his nostrils.

'Why should you remember me in particular?' I said. 'There were many of us. We were compelled to hold our hands behind our backs, and we had to take short steps.'

'Where is the sun?' he asked.

There was still no wind, but where the room opened on to

the balcony there was a slight puff of air. I loosened my clothing, still damp from the water Sayyid had given me. Moving air can cool even if its movement can hardly be felt.

The lower rim of the sun was touching the horizon and the muezzins were calling the Faithful to the fourth prayer of the day. I fetched wine and filled two glass goblets.

Sayyid said:

'In the sura called The Table the Prophet speaks disapprovingly of wine and meisar, the casting of lots.

'Yet no blame will fall upon us for what we have tasted if only we believe, do good deeds and fear Allah. This too is written in the fifth sura, the sura called The Table.

'Even in the month of fasting we may eat and drink after sunset and until a new day dawns.

'This the Prophet has written in the second sura, the sura called The Cow, and he says that Allah will make it easy for us.

'The night is over and the morning has come when there is so much light that a thread of white wool is clearly distinguishable from a thread of black.'

'I should like to accompany the small Englishman,' said Sayyid.

'You are too fat,' I answered.

'He is going on a long journey.'

'You are too old.'

'He is going to travel through unknown regions, where no one has been before, if we except those who live there and who have never been to any other place than the one in which they live.'

'You are too rich, effem.'

Sayyid Bey had many chins. His eyes were black and his hair drenched with oil. He lowered his eyes when he walked past the mirrors in the palace. He had probably never seen his own face.

'You are right,' he said. 'I am too rich. One must go on foot if one wants to see what is not seen.'

He lay down on my mat. I gave him yet another cushion and brought out the low chess table and placed it before him, carefully, so that the chessmen were not disturbed.

He asked:

'Did you say that you fell when you first set foot on Bari?'

'Before I had even taken three steps, effem.'

'How did you fall?'

'Heavily. Your harbour is built of stone.'

'Why did you fall?'

'I do not want to remember now,' I answered. 'I was prevented from taking any but very short steps. It was many years ago. How many? I do not want to count. Once I was going to be a merchant. One lives well in a Sultan's palace. It is your move, Sayyid Bey. The sun has set, it is growing dark.'

Little waves of cool air swept in through the door to the balcony.

'A new sequence of hours has begun,' I said, and lit two oil lamps.

'You are young,' said Sayyid.

'There are many ages.'

'You speak English almost as well as a Englishman or a Scot.'

'Perhaps.'

'You can write English.'

'Yes, effem.'

'You can count as the English do.'

'Did I not say a moment ago that I was once going to be a merchant?'

'Therefore you shall go in my place,' he said. 'You must go to Mac Effendi this very night.'

He rose with difficulty and left the room, but soon returned.

During his brief absence many sounds reached me. The women and the servants of the palace had begun the new sequence of hours. Some sang, the cable of the well rattled, water was poured from the bucket into pitchers, burdens were dropped on the flagstones. I heard someone slaughtering a sheep or a lamb. I heard a distant, dull hum and the near-by sound of yawning dogs. Sandals trailed and naked heels were set down on dry stones.

'Why me exactly?' I asked.

'You have explained why,' answered Sayyid.

He gave me a letter. It was not rolled, but folded upon itself and closed with a seal.

'Give it to the new Englishman, or to Mac Effendi,' he said. 'I have written it in ink. Go now!'

'The dark of night has already fallen.'

'Night is the European's best time,' he said, and sank down once more in a half-reclining position on my mat.

I moved the two lamps nearer to the chessboard and lit a third that hung by a brass chain from the ceiling.

From the palace I went down to the harbour along which I walked, and further on turned up into the town again. This was not the direct way, but in the darkness of the night it was the easiest.

Little waves were splashing against the stone quay and a hissing sound was coming from one of the foreign ships. I heard birds calling. It was dark and they were not in flight; the calls were those of sitting birds. The hour of the fifth prayer was proclaimed from the minarets.

What degree of piety is required of a bey? When had Sayyid last observed kiblah and turned towards Kaaba as he prayed?

In the harbour I stumbled over a dead man. I had lit three lamps for my master but I myself had to grope my way in darkness.

The man must have been dead. I could not hear him breathing and his body had felt stiff to my feet.

The Barites bury their dead. They do not cremate them and there are no vultures on the island.

Mac Effendi's house was close to the British Consulate. It was a large building owned by a Portuguese. I have never seen this man and I do not even know what a Portuguese looks like. Mac Effendi had lived in the house for a long time.

A number of torches were burning in the courtyard. In its centre was a brazier of glowing coals from which leapt short, flickering flames. Many men were sitting crouched near this brazier. They were either talking together in low voices or sitting silent. All were staring into the fire and some of them were smoking; none of them saw me. By reason of their poverty and insignificance they were naked, or almost naked.

Beside a flight of steps that led into the building stood six soldiers. They were tall and wore white clothing and they carried rifles and short spears. One of them challenged me.

'Salaam', I said. 'I have a letter for Mac Effendi or for Sir John, the new Englishman.'

I walked past him in a wide curve to avoid the arms he held outstretched to restrain me. One hand was tightly clenched round the muzzle of his rifle; in the other he held the necks of his spears just below the heads.

'A letter from Sayyid Bey,' I added, though he probably did not understand the language in which I spoke.

Inside the door a little group of Barites were sitting at a long table. I walked past them. I entered a second room which was well lit by paraffin lamps. It was a large room with three doors but no windows. There was a table here too, but at it only two men were seated. They did not look up and I walked past them.

The third room was empty. I walked through it and entered a corridor, one side of which opened on to a dark courtyard. The Portuguese are not content with a single courtyard, they build their houses round several. I heard leaves rustling and the falling water of a fountain. Sounds too can cool.

Then I came to a fourth room, well lit but empty. There were several doors from which to choose.

In the fifth room six men were sitting at their evening meal. One of them was Mac Effendi.

Mac Effendi has always lived in Bari. He is a Briton, or an Englishman, or an Irishman. It is difficult to distinguish between these peoples or between them and the Scots. He is the English or the British Consul and a great merchant. He seldom walks. I have seen him riding on a donkey or a pony with his toes trailing on the ground. I have seen him passing through the streets of Bari as he lay asleep and his servants carried him in a piece of cloth tied firmly to a thick bamboo pole. Apart from his face Mac Effendi's whole head is covered by short red hair.

As I closed the door behind me the six men interrupted their meal and fell silent. It was Sir John who spoke:

'What do you want?'

His question was spoken in English and I answered:

'My name is Jaffar Topan.'

'What do you want?'

'To offer my services.'

'How have you managed to get in as far as this?'

'I walked.'

'No one tried to stop you?'

'No.'

The six men had stopped eating. Three of them had been

obliged to twist round in order to see me. One seldom meets people who can tell the difference between hearing and seeing.

'No, sir,' said Sir John.

'No, sir,' I repeated.

His face was dark and shiny like the face of a well-born Arab. Little wrinkles radiated from the corners of his eyes towards his temples. His forehead was lined and his cheeks were furrowed. I had heard many stories about him and I had expected to meet a young man; not as young as I was myself, a little older than that, but not much. The man I now faced was a man who would soon be old.

It is true that there are many ages. All the same, Sir John would soon be far too old.

'Shall I get rid of him?' asked Mac Effendi.

'I need askaris and pagazis,' said Sir John.

'I am no soldier,' I said.

'You do not look like a bearer.'

'I should make a poor bearer.'

'Sir!'

'I should make a poor bearer, sir,' I said. 'I have never tried what it is like to carry things. Sir,' I added, and bowed.

'Shall I turn him out?' said Mac Effendi.

Sir John spoke again:

'Not a soldier and not a bearer. What are you good for?'

'I can both speak and write English.'

'So can I, better than you.'

'There is much that you can neither speak nor write, effem,' I said.

I corrected myself:

'There is much that you can neither speak nor write, effendim.'

Sir John's eyes are pale. He had already studied my dress, now he looked at my face just as I, a moment or two before, had looked at his. He beckoned and I went up to him. To get there I had to walk round the table.

'Turn up your sleeves,' he said.

I did as he wished and in doing so raised one hand so that it almost touched his chin.

He pointed to my neck and I opened my clothes. He looked at my feet and I took a step backwards.

'I always wear shoes,' I said, 'not sandals, not just soles, but shoes that cover the upper part of the foot.'

He wanted to know if I was an Ethiopian or an Ottoman, an Egyptian or an Indian.

'You are not a Barite,' he said.

'I have lived for a long time in Bari,' I told him. 'The air is hot and it often smells bad. I sleep readily, sir. A sleeping man does not feel the heat and even his nose sleeps. There are many sorts of Indians and there are many ways of writing, sir. I can count without the aid of an abacus. I have practised. Ten, twelve or twenty, it is all the same to me.'

'What is your name?' he asked.

'Jaffar Topan,' I answered. 'One can sleep away the heat, the day, the sun, the smells, or the long hours. It seldom rains on Bari. I am no Muslim. There are many birds on Bari. Some of them are edible, but most are no bigger than butterflies and just as inedible. There are no vultures and I have never seen a kite on Bari. Sea birds? I do not know much about sea birds. They are usually white, are they not? How much would you pay me?'

'You'll get seven pounds a year,' said Sir John.

'Your askaris get eight pounds.'

'Shall I turn him out?' asked Mac Effendi.

Sir John said:

'My bearers only get six pounds.'

'I am neither a bearer nor a soldier, effendim.'

'Eight and a half pounds.'

'To be measured by the standard of a soldier is bad,' I

said. 'I can write both English and Arabic. The symbols of the Ottoman are the more beautiful.'

'Ten pounds sterling,' he said. 'Your name is Jaffar?'

'Jaffar Topan, sir. The difference between eleven and ten is not great. It would be better to count in twelves. Twelve is a very even number.'

I gave him the letter from Sayyid Bey. He opened it but could not read it and handed it to the man nearest to him, who in his turn gave it to Mac Effendi.

'The seal has been broken,' said Sir John.

'Sealing-wax is a brittle substance and I carried the letter under my belt.'

'The Sultan's seal,' said Mac Effendi.

'Sayyid Bey wrote the letter,' I said.

'The date is today's.'

'I do not wish to correct you, sir,' I said. 'You have lived here longer than I have. But the sun has gone down, thus the letter was written yesterday. Would you like me to translate it for you? Sometimes I think I am a Barite. I shall be glad to help you, sir.'

Mac Effendi spread the letter out in front of him. 'I once lived in Stamboul,' he said to Sir John. 'I often had occasion to visit the Sublime Porte, Bab-i-Ali.'

He then translated Sayyid Bey's letter.

I left the Portuguese house. The six soldiers did not challenge me; they were only interested in people coming from the opposite direction. The many waiting men were sitting crouched as before, still waiting. The torches were out, but the brazier spread warmth.

I borrowed a lamp from a friend. I shone it over the dead man on the quay. His arms, long as those of an ape, were disfigured by elephantiasis, his legs were swollen and misshapen, his toes had no nails and his ears rested on the paving-stones of the harbour like shrunken wings.

I found a rope, drew it round the dead man's neck, pulled him across the quay and let him fall into the water. I was careful to avoid touching his body.

When I got back to the palace I found that Sayyid Bey had sent for his own pipe, a hookah with a heavy, beautifully carved stone bowl. The smoke passed through a cow's horn filled with water.

'See!' he said, pointing to the chessboard, 'my move.'

'I had anticipated it,' I answered.

I relit his pipe. It was only half smoked and the stone bowl was still warm. His eyes were glistening. He was drowsy but yet wide awake. He was drifting in a great sea of colour and he was very calm.

'Jaffar,' he said. 'When are you leaving, Jaffar Topan?'

'In a few days' time.'

'And when will you return, Jaffar?'

'I do not know if I shall ever return, effem. It is your move.'

'But if you return,' asked Sayyid, 'when will it be, Jaffar?'

'Next year, or in three years' time. Our wages are paid by the year, we have a yearly wage. A small part is paid in advance, some is paid out during the journey, most of it is not given to us until after our return to Bari. Sir John is a wise man. It is your move. Your pipe smells bad. The water is slobbering. Has it ever occurred to you that sounds too can smell? It may be several years before I return.'

'I have time to wait,' he said.

He bent over the game of chess and moved his man with a hand that was still steady.

'Much of what is otherwise forbidden is allowed on a journey,' he said. 'Where you now live you may not eat pork or the flesh of an animal that has died. You may not eat of an animal killed by the blow of an axe or by being strangled, nor of one that has died by falling from a high place. An antelope torn to pieces by a beast of prey is just as unfit to be eaten as one that has been gored to death by the horns of another at mating time. But on a journey it is different.'

Sayyid scraped out the stone bowl of his hookah, using for this purpose a long, slender silver spoon. He then filled his pipe again, with care and deliberation, putting in mostly tobacco and only a very little hashish juice.

He pushed aside the chessboard and handed me a match. I helped him to light the hookah.

'The Prophet was a human being,' he said, 'not a god or a half-god. He has therefore said that there are exceptions to almost every rule, even to many of the seemingly unconditional rules. If a traveller is forced to sin by reason of need or hunger, Allah will be merciful. I have travelled much, Jaffar. Most of all I like to travel by sea. Now you are going to travel in my place, Jaffar Topan. Allah can show leniency in all things. There is but one exception. He will not tolerate other gods beside Him. Not even a traveller in need can count upon His mercy in such a case. This is written in the Prophet's fourth sura.'

I rearranged several of his cushions and put away the chessboard, carefully, so that the chessmen were not disturbed. I relit his pipe. Tobacco moistened by hashish juice burns sluggishly.

'Travel is a form of piety,' he said. 'Certain words come into my mind. "The pious have been driven from their homes by trouble and anxiety." A wise man, Jaffar. A sufi? "Sorrow has its citadel in the hearts of these travellers." I have travelled much. It must have been a sufi who wrote of the piety of travel and of the sorrow in the travellers' hearts.'

His eyes were shining. He was in a state of complete self-absorption, enveloped by a feeling of security and trust. He was filled with a sense of well-being. The abundance of his own nature increased and he was able to show a deep understanding of a traveller's troubles and anxieties.

'But if you are too long away, Jaffar,' he said, 'it may happen that I shall have forgotten you when you return, Jaffar Topan.'

'Many people have glorified forgetfulness,' I answered. 'That which is forgotten is easy to bear. Is there no sufi who has spoken of forgetfulness, Hasan al Basri of a thousand years ago, or the Prophet himself? I do not like the smell from your pipe, effem. Why do you draw the smoke through water? Do not smoke so hard, Sayyid. I will relight your pipe if it goes out. There are many women in this house. Would not a woman be better than Indian hemp, effem?'

Sayyid Bey spoke:

'It may happen that I shall have forgotten you if you return after too long an absence. I can remember no acknowledged words of wisdom about forgetfulness. Jaffar? I have never seen you before! What right have you to enter the palace of the Sultan of Bari? Who is Jaffar? Have I ever bidden farewell to an emissary, to one who set out upon a journey in my place? Is it possible that I can ever have needed a deputy?'

Sayyid stretched himself out upon my mat. He lay on his back and only his head was turned sideways. He held the mouthpiece of the hookah tightly between both hands as if his jaws lacked strength to hold it.

I said:

'You ask who Jaffar is. Once I was going to be a merchant and I travelled, I no longer remember where. I was very young. I came here to Bari. It was you who gave me the name of Jaffar. I stumbled and fell.

'The night has come,' I said. 'All is quiet, except for the sounds you cannot hear because you were born in a palace and because the son of a sultan grows up with numbed ears.'

Sayyid began to sweat profusely. I dried his forehead, his chin and his neck. I opened his clothes and dried his chest and shoulders. He was breathing rapidly but without difficulty. He could not have risen but his eyes were bright and clear with watchfulness. He was experiencing intense heat but he was indifferent to it. Colours streamed through him and swirled round him. He was neither fat nor heavy. He was not lying on Jaffar Topan's mat. He carried no burdens, he was very calm and he was impelled to share his own feeling of security.

'When shall we leave?' he asked.

'Not tomorrow,' I answered. 'Perhaps in a couple of days.'

'Why not tomorrow?'

'It is not we who decide, Sayyid.'

'Travel is a kind of piety.'

'Yes, effem. It is night and we must sleep. Has not the Prophet or some sufi spoken of the necessity of sleep? You have often spoken of Hasan of Basra. Where is Basra? Is it a city? Where does it lie? When did this Hasan live?'

I put out two of the lamps that were alight and I dimmed the third behind a screen.

'It is night,' I said.

Sayyid Bey was weary but his eyes were clear and he was still awake.

'Basra,' he said. 'Is it a city? I have never been there. Two great rivers meet and after they have become one they are called Shatt-al-Arab. That is where Basra lies.'

'It is night,' I said.

'When are we leaving?'

'You have plenty of time.'

'No one guides those whom Allah has allowed to go astray,' he said. 'For them there is no help.'

'No, effem,' I answered.

Laronne

I

While our expedition was in process of being organized we lived with the British Consul, who performed the duties of a host with great affability. His house stood comparatively high up and its interior was cool even during the hottest hours of the day.

Later on we moved into our cabins on board the ships. Our departure was delayed for several days, which we had to spend in idleness. I found the intense heat in the harbour very trying, but I knew I should soon grow accustomed to it. I am tall and thin, and it is well known that people of my build find it easier to adapt themselves to heat than those who are short and well covered.

Our ships, the *Avanti* and the *Second*, were iron-built and propelled by steam. The *Second* was smaller than the *Avanti* and her bows were boldly curved and shot forward in a long bowsprit, for her two masts were designed to carry sails.

The major part of our supplies had been stowed on board the *Second*, which was also to carry up to some three hundred of our Barites. The remainder, about seven hundred in all, and our Galla soldiers had been embarked on the *Avanti*, which was better suited to transport of this nature.

Sir John, Stre, Hansen and I installed ourselves on the

Avanti, but the quarters assigned to Lieutenant Smitt were on the *Second*.

Our cabins were reasonably comfortable—especially when you consider that this was not a passenger ship—and, at any rate in the stern, which was reserved for us, the ship was kept clean and tidy.

The *Avanti*'s Dutch captain spent the days of waiting in an easy chair in the shade of the awning. He seldom left this place and appeared to be enjoying the inactivity. He drank large quantities of brandy and soda and always had a bowl of grapes within reach. He was slovenly in his dress and during our stay in Bari he was visited regularly every night by women from the harbour.

II

Out of our two hundred Gallas forty were armed with Winchesters, the rest with Sniders. I brought this matter up for discussion during a conversation I had with Sir John.

'Wouldn't it have been advisable,' I said, 'to have all the Gallas armed with the same make of weapon?'

We were pacing backwards and forwards on the quarter-deck. In spite of the heat the many buttons of his frock-coat were fastened right up to the neck. He was wearing tight breeches and leather boots. To minimize the glare from the sun he had drawn his peaked cap well down over his eyes.

'Which is the better weapon?' he asked.

'It's impossible to say, sir, that a Winchester—which should in fact be called a Henry Winchester—is better than a Snider or vice versa. They both have advantages, just as the Remingtons, Enfields and Peabodies have,' I said. 'I've heard that Enfields are now being used to a great extent in the British Army.'

'You appear to be well informed in these matters, Lieutenant Laronne,' he said.

Our leader is a short man and I had difficulty in refraining from bending over him as we talked.

'On my first journey,' he said, 'my men were armed mainly with Danish muskets. They were loaded from the muzzle with powder, lead shot, small stones and bits of broken nails.'

'I have seen blunderbusses like that,' I said. 'Why, I even fired a shot from a musket once, but I don't think it was of Danish make.'

'It was more than twenty years ago now,' he said, and paused by the rail to look out over the untidy harbour that was filling again with men and children who, during the hottest hours of the day, had been sheltering in the shade of the alleys.

'As for your trial shot,' he continued, 'I hope that you were not too generous with the powder and that you did not pack the wadding too tightly.'

'If I have your permission to revert to the question of the Gallas' weapons,' I said, 'I should like to emphasize the fact that both rifles are admirable in themselves. The point at issue is that these two types require different sorts of ammunition.'

'You mean that a Snider cartridge can't be used in a Winchester?'

'And that the ammunition suitable for a Winchester can't be used in a Snider, sir.'

'The cartridge for the one is too thick for the other?'

'Or too long,' I replied.

We resumed our walk to and fro on the *Avanti*'s quarter deck.

'I want to make sure you understand my meaning,' I said. 'As things now stand we shall be obliged to take with us two sorts of ammunition. I don't think that this is advisable. I'm a professional soldier and I've seen active service under very varying conditions. It's quite natural that I should think of details of this kind.'

'Perhaps you've something to suggest, Lieutenant Laronne?'

'Not at the moment, sir,' I answered.

He stopped and turned towards me. His eyes are grey or blue and deep-set. His forehead protrudes from under the peak of his cap and his eyebrows seem to rest on little rolls of muscle. Round his eyes there is a network of fine lines and these are light, not dark, because the wrinkles by which they are formed prevent them from being as much tanned by the sun as the surrounding skin. His gaze was very steady and calm.

'Do you really believe,' he said, 'that what you tell me about the way in which the Gallas are armed is news to me? Of course I have ammunition for both Sniders and Winchesters. Both sorts have been supplied by Eley's factory in London and their quality is therefore the highest obtainable.

'By reason of your age, and according to our contract, you are my second-in-command, Lieutenant Laronne. It is your business, not mine, to ensure that our askaris have the right ammunition in their cartridge-belts when the occasion for it arises. And I presume,' he continued, 'that you clearly understand that those using a Winchester, with its up-to-date repeater mechanism, will require proportionately more ammunition than those using a Snider.'

'I only wanted to call your attention to a fact,' I said, but the little man pulled me up sharply by raising his stick.

'One moment, let me finish,' he said.

Sir John's stick is a very ordinary walking-stick with a nickel-plated handle and an iron ferrule. It is not varnished, but is made of some sort of black wood which is so hard that it is practically impossible to make any impression on it with an ordinary knife.

'Let me finish,' he said.

He resumed his pacing of the deck. His voice was quiet but a trifle displeased and stern. Lieutenant Hansen remarked on some occasion that words and sentences issue from his lips like little streams of gravel.

'You realize,' he said, 'that the way in which the Gallas are armed is not accidental. It is the result of careful deliberation and selection. I'm not a professional soldier as you are. I know of no military academy which offers training in the science of exploration. I'm a self-taught man. I can't assert that I've been on expeditions of this type any given number of times more than you have, for the simple reason that this is your first expedition, which in fact hasn't yet started.'

'You're right, of course,' I said.

'What I count upon getting from you, Lieutenant Laronne, is neither advice nor comments nor opinions. What I require above all is loyalty. Next to that I take it for granted that in any given situation you will act with all the energy that it may demand.'

During the latter part of this conversation the *Avanti*'s Dutch captain left his lounge-chair and began, like us, to stroll backwards and forwards across the deck, keeping such a short distance from us that it was impossible to mistake his intentions. Sir John, who was bending forward slightly and gazing fixedly at the deck, did not notice him.

On the whole of the voyage this man behaved with a self-assertiveness and assurance that ill became him, but which, as he was in command of the vessel, he doubtless considered quite natural. By our agreement with the company to which the ship belonged, Sir John could give him orders which, in the main, he was obliged to follow. On the other hand he was undeniably the captain of the ship, and the crew were not obliged to obey anyone else.

I am not questioning his ability as a sailor, navigator, or commander of a ship. Indeed, I have already expressed my respect for the orderliness that obtained, at least in that part of the *Avanti* reserved for us. But as an individual he was in no way calculated to reinforce the authority of the European in a tropical environment.

III

Most of the men engaged for our expedition were Barites. In all there were a good thousand of them, of whom about two hundred had been enlisted as askaris and the remainder were our pagazis, bearers, porters, attendants and so forth.

I know that Sir John set great store by his Barites, and that he frequently praised them for the part they had played in his previous expeditions. However, two days' confrontation with them had been enough to produce in me a strong impression of general untrustworthiness.

One should be wary of making sweeping evaluations of an ethnic group. But the Barites do not constitute a uniform ethnic group—quite the reverse—and our Barites are distinguished by an almost complete lack of uniformity. A number of them are very tall, others again are short. Some have fair skins, others have dark, and some are almost pitch-black. Most of them wear only small loin-cloths, but some are draped in white or striped robes in the Arab fashion. A Barite may have a broad, low forehead, but he may also have a head so narrow that it looks as if it had been squeezed together. There are short, flat noses on long, narrow faces and daringly curved hook noses under low, knobbly brows. Many wear beards, many again are either clean-shaven, or almost entirely beardless. They have only one thing in common: they all have black hair; but even this point of resemblance is illusory, for the hair they conceal is sometimes short and frizzy, sometimes short and straight, sometimes long and frizzy and sometimes long and straight. There are probably bald Barites too, though I have never seen one and—here my powers of imagination fail me—I am firmly convinced that there are also innumerable varieties of Barite baldness.

It would certainly be extraordinarily interesting to be allowed to make an ethnological study of the Barites *à la* Count Gobineau.

Lieutenant Smitt and I once had a long discussion on this very subject.

'I am well aware of the fascination of paradox,' I said. 'The consistent uniformity of diversity, for instance. It may happen, not least in the matter of military strategy, that what appears to be preposterous, if it is carried out with cool intelligence, may be of decisive importance. Our expedition has, of course, a very limited objective. We are to go in search of and relieve Kanyi Pasha. For that no great brilliance is required. All we need is patient and reliable people. Our Barites, by reason of the disparity among them, do not impress me as being reliable.'

My sceptical attitude towards the Barites was intensified by their incessant chattering. They are seldom if ever silent and they are constantly involved in disputes. They quarrel, make it up, quarrel again, make it up again continuously. They are all of them businessmen in a small way: they sell to and buy from one another whenever opportunity offers. That their commerce is confined, in the main, to things worthless in themselves, only seems to have a stimulating effect.

I do not wish to deny that our Barites did make an important contribution during the expedition, but it must be remembered that they were kept together by adverse external circumstances and a firm guiding hand.

*

We divided them into companies, each of which had its own flag, bugler and drummer. They embarked on our ships in pretty good order, the lesser part of them on the *Second* while about seven hundred trooped on board the *Avanti*. They were followed by a disorderly mob of women and children—about three hundred of them all told, as we later discovered—women who had just given birth or who were about to give birth, children who could walk and children who had to be carried.

As I have already said, our departure was postponed by several days and so long as we remained in Bari harbour it was a matter of indifference to us whether these women and children came on board or collected on the quay.

An hour or so before we left Bari I asked Sir John what I was to do about them. He shrugged his shoulders.

'I need precise directions, sir,' I said.

'Some of them will go ashore, others will come with us,' he answered.

'I'm asking,' I said, 'because in the contracts drawn up when we engaged our men nothing is said about these women and children.'

'Practically speaking all Barites are illiterate,' he answered.

'Yes, sir.'

'Marriage on Bari isn't at all what we mean by marriage.'

'It won't take long to clear the ship of unauthorized persons,' I said. 'All the same I want orders from you, sir. The people involved are after all women and children.'

'Barites have certain habits,' he said.

'I don't quite understand you, sir.'

He laid his hand on my shoulder. It was a kindly gesture which I cannot remember that he ever repeated during our long journey.

'You'll learn in time, Lieutenant Laronne,' he said, 'that of necessity one must learn to rid oneself of ingrained misconceptions. Time after time you'll meet with situations and circumstances that are entirely new to you. I believe you'll do yourself a service if, from the start, you methodically avoid any feeling of surprise.'

'I'm not sure that I know what you mean, sir,' I said.

'Of course you don't,' he replied. 'My inability to express myself clearly is well known.'

A considerable number of women and children were on board our two ships when we left Bari. I cannot say for certain how many. No list was made when we sailed, and during the voyage births and deaths caused their number to fluctuate.

IV

Our company of Galla soldiers inspired in me feelings of confidence very unlike those I entertained for the Barites. They had all the uniformity so lacking in the latter. I am not allowing myself to be guilty of a rash statement when I say that never before have I encountered a body of two hundred men that displayed such a high degree of homogeneity.

They were all tall and stately and of almost the same height. Their arms and legs bulged with muscle. They were fair-skinned in the sense that they grew darker when exposed to the sun, and each face was exactly like every other face.

There was no mistaking the fact that they were professional soldiers. They were well disciplined and well drilled. They all wore short-sleeved white shirts. Worn loose these came down to their ankles; when on duty they pulled them up in a fold over their belts so that their legs had complete freedom of movement.

These askaris had joined our expedition at an early stage and had arrived in Bari on board the *Avanti*. Owing to a temporary and short-lived indisposition I was not present when they were ceremoniously handed over to Sir John.

In addition to their rifles the Gallas were armed with spears and shields. To a modern Westerner these must appear primitive and unpractical anachronisms, and at first my reaction to them was negative. I later revised my opinion, though I have some difficulty in defining why I did so. It was, to some extent, owing to the fact that their shields and spears emphasized the uniformity of these Gallas and thereby their solidarity.

Galla shields are small and made of raw oxhide. They are circular in shape and very light. I measured the diameter of a considerable number. It was obvious that efforts had been made to produce approximate but not complete similarity. The smallest of them measured barely forty-three inches, the largest forty-eight. The oxhide was quite untreated and was stretched tightly over the frame. To the touch it felt like a drumhead. This shield was carried fastened to the forearm.

The spear had a short shaft, never exceeding four feet in length. The head measured about twenty inches and was forged of surprisingly hard iron. It had no barbs and reminded one chiefly of a crude two-edged knife. Each Galla carried a bunch of three spears.

The Galla captain was called Dajatsj. By way of adornment his shield had attached to it a piece of lion's mane, so long that it trailed on the ground when the shield was not held aloft.

The colours of this company of Gallas were green like those of the Barite soldiers. The other companies had red, white, and blue flags.

Lieutenant Smitt made a large number of drawings of these Gallas.

'They're extremely decorative,' he said, 'and they sit still long enough for me to finish my sketches.'

'They'll probably acquit themselves well in other ways too,' I said.

'I'm sure of it,' he answered. 'Have you noticed the determined expression on their faces? I used to paint in oils a good deal; now I only draw.

'As you know, Lieutenant Laronne,' he went on, 'I'm really a biologist, or rather a zoologist, but I enjoy drawing.'

Smitt was rather older than Hansen, but anyone who did not know them might easily have supposed him to be the younger of the two.

'These Gallas are really decorative,' he said, laying out a number of his drawings on the cabin floor and on his table. Our conversation took place in his cabin on board the *Second*.

'What about the Barites?' I asked.

'In a way they're more interesting,' he answered. 'But as a rule they're unwilling to pose. They move away if they see me approaching with my sketching-pad.'

Jaffar Topan

I was once going to be a merchant. Now they had dressed me in a striped linen shirt and full breeches that came below the knee. They had seated me at a table on the deck of the smaller of the two ships, they had given me a book and a pen and I had become a moonshee, a scribe.

Beside me sat Lieutenant Hansen. He was wearing a white hat with a white neck-shield hanging down behind. Past us filed a stream of naked Barites bearing British riches.

Hansen called out the contents of their burdens. He was sitting on a high stool and the bearers paused by him to let him examine what they carried and, because his stool was high, there was no need for them to crouch. These Englishmen think of everything.

Bales of cloth, sacks of clothing, ropes, tents, picks, axes, spades, boxes full of nails, biscuits, rice, flour of both wheat and maize, dried meat, dried fish, tinned meat, live hens in wicker baskets. For more than an hour the men carried past us coils of copper and brass wire, beds for Sir John and his lieutenants, saucepans, crockery, wash-basins, glasses, weapons, boxes of ammunition, folded sheets of lead, pieces of leather, small barrels of tar, wax, paraffin, pearls and shells in oblong bags of chamois-leather, European instruments and metal medicine chests, knives, some short, some long, so long that they looked like short swords.

Hansen called out the names and I wrote them down, feeling more like a merchant than a scribe. We were sitting shaded from the sun but, nevertheless, the white paper of my book dazzled me. The ink dried on the pen and my damp hand left a dark mark on the paper.

I said to Sayyid Bey:

'Sir John has foreseen all that he may need. I know of nothing that he has overlooked.'

Sayyid answered:

'One can never tell what an Englishman may have overlooked. When are you leaving?'

'In a couple of days, effem, tomorrow, or the day after tomorrow, or the day after that. A boy tried to steal a handful of pearls. We have finished loading unless something yet remains that must also be loaded. I would never have believed that I should come to miss the palace in Bari.

'They are great arithmeticians,' I continued. 'They constantly apply new measurements to their riches. A bale of cloth is a bale, but a bale can be changed into dhotis and a dhoti can be expressed in feet. Dhotis can also be dollars. Five dhotis are seven and a half dollars. How many feet is a dollar? Are you listening, effem? They buy their bales of cloth in dollars, they pay their wages in pounds sterling. Cloth is also reckoned in loads. A man's load is two frasilahs or seventy-three pounds. There are rather more than two pounds in a kilogramme. How many kilogrammes does a dollar weigh? What will happen to the one who tried to steal a handful of pearls?'

'I do not concern myself about thieves,' answered Sayyid.

'One must be well equipped when one is going on a long journey,' he said. 'Englishmen are always well equipped, so are the Germans and the Portuguese.'

'I have never seen a Portuguese, effem,' I said.

'Once, very long ago, they conquered the whole of Bari,' answered Sayyid. 'The price was many dead. For more than a hundred years Bari was a Portuguese port. Then they were driven away from here by the Sultan who was my ancestor. The price of that in dead was even greater. I do not remember whether I am his descendant in the seventh or the ninth generation, but I could reckon it out.

'Another time, and that too very long ago, the Portuguese set fire to a well-wooded island. It lay far out in the ocean and it burned for seven years. During those years the smoke that rose in an enormous pillar was an excellent navigation mark for the vessels that sailed in the neighbouring waters.'

Laronne

I

After we left our comfortable quarters with the British Consul we took our meals on the *Avanti*'s quarter-deck, under the awning. We did not assemble for dinner, our chief meal of the day, until darkness had fallen.

It became apparent that Sir John was anxious that our meals, and of course more especially our dinners, should be dignified by correct behaviour, not only when taken within four walls in a comfortable room, but also later on when we were living under conditions of camp-life.

The places that Sir John assigned to us at our first meal together we continued to occupy for the whole of the journey. Our leader sat at one end of the table and we, his lieutenants, sat facing each other, two on either side. My place was on Sir John's right; beside me sat Hansen and opposite me Dr Stre with Smitt beside him. So long as we were aboard the *Avanti* her Dutch captain, who shared our meals, sat at the other end of the table opposite Sir John. While we were actually at sea Smitt, of course, was absent from our table, as he lived on board the *Second*, our other ship.

We were waited upon at table by one of Sir John's attendants, a youth from Amman called Said. He was sixteen or seventeen years old. He spoke perfectly comprehensible English and he was always attentive and polite. He was by no means a fully trained waiter, but this was wholly compensated for by his good manners and his perpetually smiling face. He was strikingly slender, one should perhaps say thin. He looked as if he might be of Jewish origin, but he wore Turkish trousers, an Egyptian blouse, and a red fez with a black tassel and, so far as we could judge, he was a Muslim.

Our conversation at table was conducted by our leader with determination and a regal air. He commented upon the happenings of the day and asked us many questions, most of them of a kind that could, or should, only be answered by an affirmative or a negative. Sir John must be described as a taciturn man, but sometimes at dinner, by way of contrast, he would hold forth on subjects he had much at heart, with a flow of words that almost gave what he had to say the air of miniature lectures rather than leisurely table-talk.

At our last evening meal in Bari harbour we had soup, fish, and boiled mutton. The fish put one in mind of carp, but had shorter, coarser, and more easily removable bones. The relationship between the soup and the mutton was easily discernible. The sweet consisted of a very sickly cake, dripping with honey. With this meal we drank sherry throughout, but beside each place was a glass intended for the soda-water with which we could quench our thirst, and of which Niederselters had made us a present of two hundred sealed bottles.

Sir John addressed us:

'I'm convinced, gentlemen, that you're accustomed to a much better table than this. All the same our meal can't be condemned as quite *pauvre*. I can assure you that later on you will remember it as a banquet.'

'You've already prepared us for a very limited diet in the future,' I said.

'During my first expeditions,' he continued, 'I didn't set much store by what I ate. I had what my pagazis ate and I drank what they drank. If by any chance you've read my books you'll know that for long periods of time I was troubled by fevers, exhaustion, colic and other digestive disturbances. Generally speaking, the fevers were the most troublesome, but I'm more frightened of suffering again from attacks of colic. During my subsequent journeys I was wise enough to preserve, as far as possible, Western habits in the matter of food, and this benefited both my own health and that of my companions. Unfortunately opportunities of hunting suitable game seldom occur.

'It's all the more fortunate that we now have access to excellent and very long-lasting tinned foods. With all due deference, smoked or salted meat can't be compared to the modern tinned varieties. As you'll realize, I've had ample opportunity to follow developments in this field. The tastiest products are those manufactured in Chicago and their quality is also very even. Two Swiss opened a factory in the Argentine some years ago, and their products too are excellent. South American cattle give the best meat in the world in my opinion. It's fat, close-grained, and easy to carve. The fat is well distributed in the muscle-tissue. Nowadays you can also buy tinned butter.'

'What you say about muscle being interspersed with fat is quite correct,' said Dr Stre. 'But doesn't the same apply to all cattle, even to European? In pigs, for example, fat is very differently distributed.'

'Of course,' answered Sir John, 'the excellent quality of South American meat doesn't depend on where the fat is found, but on the fact that it occurs in greater quantity. We have no tinned butter among our stores. No satisfactory method of preservation has yet been discovered and its keeping qualities are therefore strictly limited.'

When we had finished our meal we left the table and made ourselves comfortable in the vessel's basket-chairs ready for coffee. Sir John was very fond of coffee and consumed large quantities of it. I resigned myself to this habit which, especially in the matter of evening coffee, required some self-sacrifice on my part, as it kept me from sleeping well at night. Moreover, the coffee served was of the Turkish variety, sweet and black, and so thick that one had to keep it rotating by a rapid circular movement of the hand in order to drink it to the bottom.

My aversion to coffee was shared by our Dutch captain. He, however, did not see anything to prevent him from leaving his cup untouched. He used to sink down into his basket-chair with a glass of brandy and water in his hand.

'During this enterprise we shall have to rely very largely on the luck of the chase,' said Sir John. 'We can't increase our numbers beyond a certain limit. We can't engage enough bearers to transport all the tinned foods that would have been desirable.'

'I've always been very interested in hunting,' said Hansen. 'I wasn't more than ten or twelve when I had my first shotgun. It was a short, large-bore weapon, but light to handle.'

'You must clearly understand,' continued our leader, 'that an expedition of the kind on which we are about to embark is a very demanding undertaking. It has a purely practical side—it must be carried through to a conclusion. That is a task for all of us. It has also a theoretical side—it must be planned and organized. That, in the main, is my business as the responsible leader of the expedition. In all important respects this latter task is now completed. I think I may assert without boasting that I have taken all the preparatory measures that are necessary.'

'We're convinced that you have, Sir John,' I said.

'All the preparatory measures that are possible,' he added, stretching out for his pipe and lighting it. He was an ardent smoker. His pipe was almost always hanging out of his mouth, but he never appeared to inhale. I had noted the somewhat amusing fact that he never smoked during our rather protracted evening meals, neither between the main course and the sweet, nor before we had sat down to coffee. When we did so he took out his pipe, his tobacco-pouch and his matches, but he never touched them until he had drunk a cup of coffee or more often two cups. When he did, Dr Stre would light a cigar. His smokes were not of a good brand. They flared up when he lit them and the saltpetre in them sputtered.

'Our preparations require knowledge, experience, and concentration,' said Sir John. 'I'm constantly having to deliberate, to weigh things up, and I must never allow my powers of cool calculation to lapse. It's very probable that I'm now talking about matters of which you have so far been unaware.'

'I should be grateful if you could express yourself rather more explicitly,' said Dr Stre.

Stre was one of Sir John's lieutenants, just as I, Smitt, and Hansen were. All the same it became apparent from the start that, by reason of his medical qualifications, he aspired to a privileged position, an ambition that was in no way deflected by the fact that I was the man next to Sir John, the commander of the expedition *en second.*

Our leader replied:

'The choice of my colleagues and of the other members of the expedition can be said to be part of the final phase of these preparations. By the time you came on the scene, gentlemen, my many deliberations and calculations were a chapter that was already largely completed.

'The aim of our expedition is simple,' he continued. 'We are to seek out and relieve Kanyi Pasha. We know in what area he is to be found, and we shall find him if he is still alive. But we have not only to find him, we have also to relieve him. It's here that we encounter the first complication. What does Kanyi Pasha require? What are the necessities of which he stands most in need? Our information on this subject is very scanty. In making my preliminary assessment of his needs I've been obliged to use my imagination and my knowledge of the geographical and political conditions that obtain in the area in which he now is.

'An expedition of this kind is a matter of figures. It's something of a fine art in the same sense that mathematics can be regarded as a fine art. It's easy enough to draw up a list of what is required. It's also quite easy to estimate the total weight of these requisites. It's considerably more difficult to reduce this list to proportions that lie within the scope of actual achievement. What we have to transport to the Pasha by way of supplies weighs—even after a number of deductions have been made—considerably more than seven tons.'

'We should require more than two hundred and fifty bearers for that,' I said.

'Your figure is correct, but theoretical,' answered our leader. 'The exact number can't be fixed until we know something about the sort of conditions obtaining in the areas through which the expedition will have to pass. Moreover, bearers require leaders and these in their turn demand still more bearers. The expedition has to be protected by askaris. As a rule soldiers can't carry more than their weapons; therefore soldiers require an additional number of bearers. It really is a most interesting problem, quite mathematical in character. The more bearers and porters we have, the more soldiers we require; the more soldiers, the more bearers. Have I expressed myself with sufficient clarity, Dr Stre?

'Do you understand now,' he went on, 'why I regard the preparations as the most difficult part of the expedition? Even so I have still said nothing about the most troublesome factor of all: the stretch of country we shall have to traverse from the moment we leave the ship until we actually encounter the Pasha. Dr Stre, how do you measure distance?'

'In miles or kilometres, of course,' answered the doctor, 'but I gather, sir, that you have in mind a more relevant standard of measurement.'

'The metric system is an admirable invention,' answered Sir John. 'I willingly admit that I have always felt a certain repugnance for other systems. When I was young I had some difficulty in making a distinction between a British mile and a London mile and their equivalents in feet, and I found it almost impossible to remember whether a statute mile was the same as a British mile or a London mile. Wasn't it during the French Revolution that the metric system was introduced?

'During my many long journeys,' he continued, 'I've kept, day by day, a precise and careful record of events, and I know that the more theoretically-minded geographers have attached great value to it. In these notes I always used the metric system as my standard of measurement.

'But when it comes to measuring the length of any proposed expedition one must make use of other units than kilometres and miles. The thing that matters is not the actual distance to be covered but the time that will be required. I'm speaking from experience.

'On one of my journeys,' he continued, 'I covered one thousand three hundred kilometres in one hundred and three days, that is an average of thirteen kilometres a day. On another occasion it took me ten days to advance a distance of sixty kilometres. In savannah country distance contracts. Two years ago I marched two hundred and thirty kilometres in six days. In forests distance expands, and grows greater the denser the forest becomes. It may take an hour to advance four hundred metres. There are forests which have a depth of ten thousand hours. The distance that an expedition can accomplish should be reckoned in days, and effectively a day is, at the most, seven hours.

'A further complication in estimating distance is the fact that the nature of the country to be traversed is not the only decisive factor. The number of persons in a caravan is also important. The fewer the men the shorter the distance, the larger the expedition the greater it becomes.'

At this moment the *Avanti*'s Dutch captain rose to his feet.

'You ought to have been a sailor, sir,' he said. 'You would have enjoyed it. At sea there are neither miles, nor feet, nor kilometres. It is true that we do not measure distance in hours or days, but we do measure it in minutes.'

He raised his empty glass, bowed to Sir John, bowed to the rest of us and then once more to our leader. Thereupon he departed.

Sir John spoke again:

'I am not without a purpose in trying to give some account of the preparations I have made for this expedition. In spite of the fact that the books I have written about my previous expeditions have appeared in very large editions, I am well aware that I am a poor hand at telling a story. I hope, all the same, that I have succeeded in making it plain to you that I have carried out the preparatory measures with methodical deliberation, aided by my not inconsiderable experience. I have gone into everything in detail, so far as it is humanly possible to do so.'

'Your characterization of a relief expedition as a mathematical problem was very fascinating,' said Dr Stre.

Sir John continued:

'Lieutenant Laronne has questioned the advisability of our Gallas being armed some with Sniders, others with Winchesters. He has pointed out that the ammunition for the one is unsuitable for the other and vice versa.'

I interrupted him:

'My objection was in itself justifiable. On the other hand your explanation was unassailable and perfectly convincing, sir.'

'I am not trying to put you in your place, Laronne,' he said. 'I am merely using you as an example. Since none of you have taken any part in the preparations, none of you can have any idea of how thorough they have been. Winchester or Snider? This has been a matter of weighing up alternatives, a question of short-term firing efficiency against long-term transport of heavy loads of ammunition.'

'Can't we consider the discussion closed?' I said.

'Not quite.'

'You mean, sir?'

'What I require, gentlemen,' he replied, 'is not your advice, or your comments, but your loyalty. Your loyalty is the prerequisite for the fortunate outcome of our expedition. I should be grateful if you would try to appreciate the purport of my words.'

II

Sir John filled and relit his pipe. The basket-chairs were so placed that he was sitting at an angle to us, and we were therefore unable to see his face in the light of the match.

'I'm in the habit of describing myself as a thoughtful person,' he said, 'but I'm very far from being a philosopher. My studies have been fragmentary, to say the least of it. For instance, I find it difficult to be articulate in academic circles.'

'You mean, sir?' I said.

'While reflecting on practical matters I have recently been led to ponder over two circumstances.'

'Which are?'

'When I first heard of Kanyi Pasha's plight,' said Sir John, 'it was obvious to me that he must be rescued. It was obvious, not because he was an Ottoman official in a prominent position, but because he was by origin a European, and must still—notwithstanding his title and his name—be regarded as a European.'

'Wasn't that quite right and proper, sir?' asked Lieutenant Smitt.

'Of course it was right and proper,' answered Sir John, 'but has it ever been taken for granted that, for instance, Arabs would hasten to help a fellow Arab, should he find himself in difficulties in a very distant place? Have you ever heard of the Indians equipping an expedition to relieve an Indian, or the Chinese relieving a Chinese? And what of the Japanese, the Malayans, the Mongolians?'

'I've not travelled much, particularly not in comparison with yourself,' said Dr Stre, 'and my knowledge of history is limited. But isn't this a question of Western economic resources and Western means of communication?'

'It's first and foremost a question of Western morality,' said Sir John.

'You mentioned two circumstances,' said Lieutenant Hansen.

'Our task is therefore to find and relieve Kanyi Pasha,' said our leader. 'It is a difficult task. This expedition is the largest I've ever led. It's probably one of the largest forces ever assembled that hadn't a military objective. For a long time now I've devoted all my attention to it, and it will demand all my strength and energy for an unforeseeable length of time to come. Our task is not without danger. I carefully pointed out the element of danger to each one of you before you signed the contract.'

'We're all prepared to testify to that,' I said.

'The relief of Kanyi Pasha is our objective. Our expedition is merely the means. While making the preparations for it I have noticed how my interest has shifted from the Pasha to the expedition itself.'

Sir John turned his chair so that he now sat facing us. 'You're a surgeon, aren't you?' he said to Dr Stre.

'It was primarily a surgeon that you required, sir, wasn't it?' replied our doctor.

'As a surgeon you must frequently have observed a shift of interest such as I have described,' he said. 'Surgical intervention as such, its technique and its method, is the important thing. The person performing an operation may be quite satisfied even if the patient dies.'

'I can't concur with your supposition, sir,' said Dr Stre. 'For that matter surgical measures are, as a rule, extremely trivial. A splinter removed from under a nail, a wound that has to be sewn up, or an insignificant, though doubtless painful, abscess. You open the latter with a neat little incision, but you know that it would have burst of itself, possibly in a matter of hours.'

Said, the boy from Amman, arrived with two lighted paraffin lamps. It was quite dark in spite of the fact that it was only early evening. But with darkness had come increasing and liberating coolness. Gentle breezes blew from the continent to the west, the sail-cloth above us flapped and we could hear the water swish-swoshing between the hull of the ship and the quay. Said hung one lamp from one of the ropes holding the awning, the other he placed on the deck quite near my chair.

'Do you mean that you are beginning to lose interest in Kanyi Pasha?' said our doctor.

'Of course not. But if you asked me his age I shouldn't be able to answer until I had looked it up in my notebook. I can't remember his real name in full. I should be almost entirely unable to answer if you asked me about his contributions to science. I could no longer give you a detailed account of why he should be where he now is. The bulk of my notes, my letters and other papers and documents have been left behind in my house at Brindisi.'

'When I make notes,' said Dr Stre, 'I uncouple my memory and rely on the written word. Making notes is really a method of forgetting.'

Sir John spoke again:

'I was trying to point out what to me is a noteworthy shift of interest from the object of the expedition to the expedition itself. It was not my intention that the conversation should lead to an atmosphere in which confidences are exchanged, a thing I do not care for, and which I do not regard as desirable.'

Soon after this Sir John rose and went below deck.

'I feel sure,' remarked Dr Stre, 'that in future our leader will succeed in safeguarding himself against an undesirably confidential atmosphere.'

Jaffar Topan

The thousand or more Barites had to be divided into companies and their names written down in a book, company by company.

How many are the Barites on the island of Bari, and how few are their names!

Sir John read aloud from his notes and I wrote. I know that one language is one language and another is another and that they are separated by a wall.

'Words can be interpreted, effendim,' I said. 'Sometimes you must replace one word by several words; at other times many words can be replaced by one. People who use many words are often easier to interpret than those who use few. The interpreter who travels from place to place has the best of it. He soon leaves behind him those he has misunderstood. Names are difficult to translate.'

The names of the thousand or more Barites had to be written down in English characters. Sir John dictated them, letter by letter, and in this way they were translated and assembled in my book like foreigners.

'The Barite characters are more beautiful than the English,' I said. 'There are not many Barites who can read and write.'

Sir John distinguished between the many whose names

were the same by noting down their age or approximate age, or by adding their father's name, or a surname, or the name of the place from which they came. The last was only possible for those who did not live in the city of Bari.

The second day was far advanced before the last name was written down. It took me just as long to draw up two copies.

The Barites we had enrolled were divided into seven companies, and each company was given a number and a captain.

'Figures create order,' I said. 'I like figures. There was a time when they intended me to become a merchant.'

We were sitting in a room next to Sir John's cabin. We were out of the sun, but although the ship was in motion, there was not a breath of air, for you could not open the port-holes.

During the first day's dictation Lieutenant Laronne had to retire on several occasions. On two of them he was away for a long time and once, when he returned, he had changed his clothes. Sir John waited patiently for him. The two of them sat at one desk, I at another.

No. 3 Company consisted of rather more than two hundred Barites, and they had been chosen with care, for they were the soldiers. All the other Barites were assigned to companies in the order in which they had arrived at Mac Effendi's house and been engaged as pagazis.

'Why not sort them, sir?' I asked. 'No two men are alike. It is true that they are all bearers, but there the resemblance ends. They do not only vary in strength. I should like to group them according to type, to draw them up in a line and work from one end to the other, seeing to it that the difference was greatest between those nearest the extremities and least between those standing closest to each other. After all, the companies are numbered.'

It was stuffy in the room next to Sir John's cabin. The days were long. Sir John went to bed late and rose early. He never rested during the hottest hours of the day.

'Not now,' he said, 'not during a voyage. We eat and drink more than we require. We do not walk, for the most part we sit. It's warm here but it's blowing up on deck and the air is invigorating.'

Sir John was kind in the way that old men are often kind, very much as Sayyid Bey was kind. Neither of them was yet old, but they were both considerably older than I was.

There are also old men who live in want. Humbleness is not the same thing as kindness.

Lieutenant Laronne, Sir John's vakeel, was slit-eyed and had high cheekbones. He found it hard to listen and he seldom sat still. He was reticent and he was always washing himself.

The seven captains, the leaders of the seven companies, had been selected with far more hesitation and care than the soldiers of No. 3 Company. This had been done in consultation between Sir John, Mac Effendi and Lieutenant Laronne. They were all Muslims and Barites.

'No two men are alike,' I said to Sir John. 'Any sort of person you please may be a Muslim. Any sort of person may be a Barite. Sometimes I think that I too was born on Bari.'

Salaam spoke English almost as well as a Briton. His face was smooth and his arms rounded. He had once acted as gun-bearer to a German traveller. His voice was shrill and he bowed deeply. Even his name was a salutation: salaam. Though his hips were as rounded as those of a eunuch he was impetuous and eager. Salaam was the leader of No. 1 Company, the smallest in numbers.

Kingiri was the captain of No. 2 Company, the largest. He was probably the oldest of the Barite leaders. He wore a loin-cloth and a short shirt. He had a leopard skin that had been cut in pieces and sewn together in such a way that he could carry it thrown across one shoulder.

Kingiri's head was peculiarly small, the smallest head I have ever seen, and the crown of it was covered by a crop of short, wiry grey hair. His eyes were old and inflamed, and they gleamed in the sunshine. He had seen a great deal. His face was rugged and very wrinkled. He had experienced many things. His mouth had been enlarged. It must have been done when he was still a child. Two slits had been made across his cheeks, the one from the left corner of his mouth towards his left ear, the other from the right corner towards the right ear. His left hand had suffered an injury. All that was left was the thumb and a bare half of the palm.

The captain of the two hundred carefully selected Barite soldiers was called Halmadi. He had once been bought by a Barite merchant and come to Bari in his youth. He maintained that he was originally a Syrt. I know of no one who has ever heard of this people.

'There are many different peoples,' I said to Sir John. 'They are not easy to keep apart for one who has travelled as little as I have or met so few of them. They call themselves by one name, their neighbours use another when referring to them, and this name too changes, step by step, the further away from them they are. Words and sentences can be translated from one language to another, but if you translate a name you change it.'

Halmadi had visited Mecca many times and enjoyed talking about it. To start with he had journeyed there as his master's deputy, but afterwards he had gone there as a pilgrim in his own right. He wore a threadbare woollen mantle, and he could just as well have been a sufi as a Syrt, this people of whom no one has ever heard.

After the death of his master, the Barite merchant, Halmadi, had married his youngest wife and driven away the other three, although the Prophet had once owned fourteen wives over and above his innumerable concubines.

He had no liking for trade and had taken service first with Englishmen, then with Germans. His wife was dead and he was alone, but he still owned a large house and many servants. Now he was the captain of Sir John's Barites. His nose was straight and he had no neck.

No. 7 Company was the second smallest, having only ninety-eight men. Its leader was called Abdul. Because of the commonness of this name he had several surnames. To begin with he was called Abdul the Great, because he was taller than most of the others. Later he was called Abdul the Small for the same reason.

As it happened the task assigned to his company was that of carrying the boats for the expedition. These boats were made of steel and so constructed that they could be taken apart when they had to be transported across dry land. Each section required two bearers and the total number of sections was forty-nine. Sir John was therefore obliged to ensure that Abdul's company always numbered ninety-eight pagazis, all healthy and able-bodied enough to carry their loads. It was owing to this fact that the boat-bearers' captain got his final name: Abdul the Ninety-ninth.

His ears were pierced and weighed down by polished pieces of rhinoceros horn and between his legs hung a pouch filled with the testicles of mountain-deer.

The captains of Companies No. 4, No. 5, and No. 6 were called Sjimba, Joffar, and Kami. They might have been brothers. They were unlike each other as brothers usually are, and all the same they looked alike. Sjimba was Kami's senior by exactly as much as Joffar was his junior. They all had broad hips and heavy legs, and they all kept their eyes half shut in the dark. To anyone who prefers noses of another shape, their noses were hideously flat. Only Sjimba could write.

These three had all been born in the city of Bari. They had grown up there and you could not put any trust in the stories they told of the journeys they had made.

Sjimba had a green fez that had kept its colour, but grown soft with age. He often carried it tucked into his sash. Nearly all the Barites wore a sash round their waists made of kaniki, an Indian material, blue in colour.

'People are fascinating,' I said to Sir John. 'It is an adventure just to look at them. One could lie on a soft divan and let a thousand people pass by, or be led by, and it would be like making a long journey.'

There was yet another group of Barites in addition to the seven companies. This consisted originally of twenty-eight men and boys who, solely by reason of their number, could not form a separate company. They acted as attendants. gun-bearers, cooks, water-carriers, buglers and tent-riggers to Sir John and his lieutenants. They did not need a captain of their own, but they had a spokesman. He was called Said, and came from Amman. He held this office as a matter of course for he was Sir John's attendant and gun-bearer. He was still only a youth.

The expedition's No. 8 Company was formed by the Galla soldiers. They called themselves by this name and they were Copts, but not Ethiopians. They had arrived in Bari on board Sir John's ship.

Names are difficult to translate. The Gallas came from a distant place and they were therefore surrounded by mystery. They had long hair like Sikhs, but they wore shirts, not short trousers. Many of them had iron bracelets, but instead of swords they carried spears.

Their captain was called Dajatsj. He had not been appointed by Sir John but had held the office from the start.

In spite of their green flag most of the Gallas wore a chain round their necks from which hung a cross. Their language was easy to learn as they used few words. For the same reason it was hard to translate.

The Galla captain's name was not only a name, it was also a title and he had once been in the service of Negus Todros. This may have been why many people believed the Gallas were really Ethiopians.

It took two days to draw up the list of our men. I was set to make two copies, and each one took me a day. If the list were lost these copies would be valuable, and if one of the copies too were lost, the one that remained would be more valuable than ever.

Laronne

I

On our second night aboard the *Avanti* there was a fierce outbreak of violence. I was awakened by someone knocking loudly on my door. He did not answer my questions but, as I could hear noises and shouts in the distance, I dressed hastily and hurried up on deck.

It was very dark. There was a cool, almost chilly wind and the vessel rose and fell rhythmically on the waves. The helmsman on the captain's bridge understood neither French nor English and he only shook his head. Our Dutch captain was asleep and his chief mate was not there either.

The rumpus was coming from the bowels of the ship. I tried to question some women who were sheltering close to one of the *Avanti*'s superstructures. Two of them were veiled and none of them answered. They crouched together in the darkness, away from the night wind.

As I ran forward I stumbled over something, a thick, rigid stump of rope a metre long. I took it with me as a weapon.

A tight cluster of Galla soldiers, faintly illuminated by a lamp, were standing beside the forward companion-way down to the middle deck. When they noticed me they silently made way for me to pass, but closed up again behind me.

The steep ladder was crammed with Gallas, their white backs forming an obstructive wall. Those highest up were pushing downwards, while those lower down were clearly trying to resist, and hold their comrades back.

I could not make myself heard. It was only by kicking and hitting out with the stump of rope that I succeeded in making any headway.

The forward middle deck—I am not certain that this is the right term—was a large room, almost square, stretching from one side of the vessel to the other. It had a low ceiling from which hung a solitary paraffin lamp, its only source of light.

The room was a snake-pit of fighting Barites and Gallas. The white garments of the latter, who were clearly in a minority, made it easy to pick them out among the many hundred naked black bodies, glistening with sweat and oil.

It appeared to me that the fighting was going on in a peculiarly silent manner, the only sounds that accompanied it being the tramp of naked feet and an occasional half-smothered or interrupted shout.

My efforts to attract the attention of the combatants failed, and I very soon received a sharp blow on the back of my neck which brought me to the ground. Many people trod on me, particularly on my arms, and, before I could get to my feet and recover my equilibrium, I was dragged into the centre of the room. I hit about me with my stump of rope and felled a number to the floor.

Then the paraffin lamp was smashed and went out. It may be that in the dark the intensity of the fighting increased. For those unaccustomed to injure and wound it is easier to strike when you cannot see the man you are hitting.

In the dark I was hurled to the floor and wounded in the back by a knife or the point of a spear. Something heavy fell on top of me and I was unable to rise.

*

Light returned when Hansen and Dr Stre came down the ladder, each carrying a lamp. They were followed by Sir John, also carrying a lamp, which he handed to Hansen as he squeezed past him. He was holding in his hand a brass staff, perhaps two feet long. This staff fulfilled some purpose on the ship, though I cannot remember what, and he had probably picked it up on his way from his cabin.

He paused for a moment on the lowest rung and a handful of Gallas formed up behind him, their spears and shields raised. Thereupon the fighting ceased.

Sir John walked to and fro between the men, from one side of the ship to the other, a couple of times. More lamps were lit. The Barites huddled against the walls of the room. Most of the Gallas climbed the steep ladder with dignity and without haste.

I sat up when Sir John stopped beside me. A Barite was lying prostrate over my legs. Two of the Gallas tried to make him stand up, but he was as floppy and boneless as a big rag-doll. His head hung down limply between his shoulders and he was not breathing. He was quite naked except for a short jacket. His chin was covered with clots of blood but there was no sign of a wound.

Sir John opened one of his eyes with his thumb. The eyeball was already dry and the eye remained open.

II

The wound in my back was a good ten inches long. It started close to my spine on the left-hand side and ended close to my right hip-bone. The lower part of the wound was fairly deep, but not so deep that Dr Stre considered it necessary to put in any stitches. It was treated with iodine, but this did not prevent some infection setting in near the hip. For a short time I had a high fever and for a few days I was, generally speaking, ill and debilitated.

I was obliged to lie on one side or on my stomach and if, in my sleep, I turned on to my back it woke me up.

I never had a chance of seeing the wound. There was a mirror in my cabin but it was fixed to the wall far too high up. The screws had rusted fast in the wooden panel and I broke a knife when I tried, unsuccessfully, to loosen them. It is very surprising that brass, or at least galvanized, screws are not used on a ship.

On the day after the uproar Sir John visited me in my cabin. We drank coffee together which was served on a tray by his attendant Said.

After he had asked permission to light his pipe he said:

'I appreciate energy and fearlessness, Lieutenant Laronne.'

I bowed, in so far as a prostrate man can bow.

'I should like to ask a couple of questions,' he said.

'I shall be happy to answer them if I can, sir.'

'Have I rightly understood what actually happened? You went down the ladder and found a crowd of our men engaged in a violent struggle?'

'That is so.'

'You intervened?'

'Of course, sir.'

After having got his pipe going he continued:

'You were alone?'

'I did not count those present,' I replied. 'There were probably at least five hundred men. The light was bad and it was very crowded.'

A fleeting smile crossed Sir John's face. His smile is a rare occurrence. I do not discount the possibility that I may have been mistaken. He has an ample moustache which hangs down so far that it partially conceals his mouth.

'How were you armed?' he asked.

'Someone woke me up,' I answered. 'I dressed and went up on deck. I did not of course know what was going on. I found a stump of rope. It was rigid and thick and easy to get a grip on.'

'Had you any idea of how you were going to put a stop to the trouble?'

'That is a very difficult question to answer, sir,' I said.

He told Said to pour out yet another cup of coffee. He was sitting very stiff and upright on his chair. He had put his cap on his knees and held his cup and saucer poised in one hand.

'I appreciate your fearlessness,' he said. 'All the same, I shall count upon you to intervene rather differently in any similar incidents in future.'

III

Sir John had a birthday and invited us all to a dinner to celebrate it. This took place on the very day that my wound became septic. I had to sit on a stool though I should really have been glad of something to lean against. The fact that I had no appetite was understood and respected both by my host and by my fellow guests.

The day was ushered in by a salute that our Dutch captain ordered should be fired from a small, old-fashioned cannon we carried in the stern of the ship. It was moreover a very beautiful day. The sea was calm, the *Avanti* drove a wedge of waves through the water and the *Second* kept close to us. Her hull was as long as the *Avanti*'s but more slender. There was speed in her lines. Her bow had a daring curve and, when you looked at her, you felt that she was being held firmly in check, and that it was only with an effort that her skipper could persuade her to follow in the *Avanti*'s wake.

Lieutenant Smitt joined us at the celebration dinner. He was rowed across from his ship, a manœuvre that certainly prolonged our voyage by several hours.

It was a warm evening. The wind was blowing aft, but not hard enough to prevent the ship from keeping pace with it.

The Dutchman arrived rather late at the dinner table, which had been laid on deck under the awning. He was wearing a short-sleeved shirt. His apologies and his manner of greeting us were neither of them quite correct, either in choice of words or tone of voice. Taking into consideration his vulgarity, or rather the cause of his vulgarity, I cannot exclude the possibility that he had simply forgotten to put on his uniform jacket.

The *Avanti*'s quarter-deck was kept separate from the rest of the ship by a rope and a guard of Gallas. Both had been arranged before we left Bari. This was essential. We had over a thousand Barites and Gallas on board. However, everything was very quiet this evening. The outbreak of violence on the forward middle deck had had a sobering effect upon our men.

The Dutchman made a long and partially incoherent speech. Sir John replied, and then turned to our doctor with the abruptness that he so frequently displays.

'Dr Stre,' he said. 'I should very much like to hear your views on fevers, malaria and dysentry.'

'That's a very general question, sir. Couldn't you be a little more precise?'

'I want to know what causes them. As a doctor you must be aware that there are two alternatives from which to choose.'

'What two alternatives?'

'On the one hand miasma, on the other Dr Koch's theory regarding bacteria.'

Here our leader raised his black stick, and added:

'I have myself been laid low by at least a hundred attacks of fever in the course of my life. Most of them have been slight and of short duration. Some have been very severe.'

'Micro-organisms are very interesting,' answered Dr Stre.

'What's your opinion as a doctor of Dr Koch, or of Messrs Brunton, Fothergill and Fayrer?'

'You are referring to Robert Koch if I understand you aright, sir?'

'To tell the truth I've forgotten his Christian name.'

'He's now a professor at the University of Berlin,' said Dr Stre.

'It wouldn't surprise me to hear that Brunton and Fayrer had become professors too,' said Sir John.

We drank hot coffee. In honour of the day Said had lit four paraffin lamps and hung them up under the awning. I wished I had been able to sit in one of the restful basket-chairs, for my wound was aching.

'When I was a student I worked quite a lot with a microscope,' said Dr Stre. 'Why, I even constructed a primitive piece of apparatus for microphotography. A great deal of light was required, and the organisms died when exposed to it because of the excessive heat. That problem is now solved. But I'm not a research worker, I'm only a surgeon.'

The Dutch captain bent forward and patted Dr Stre on the knee.

'A microscope is only a telescope turned the wrong way round,' he said. 'It's certainly no kind of an instrument for navigators.'

Having said this he rose.

'I have my duties to attend to,' he said.

Before departing he examined the lamps that Said had hung up. He detached two of them and placed them on the deck.

'Merely a precautionary measure,' he said. 'I fear the awning will not tolerate exposure to excessive heat.'

'Wit manifests itself in a variety of forms,' said Dr Stre.

IV

The serious outbreak of violence on the forward middle deck had cost six men their lives. The day after Sir John's birthday we encountered rough weather and two women and a child died. The bodies were dropped into the sea by Halmadi, the captain of the Barite soldiers.

As I said before, the wound on my back occasioned firstly fever and secondly a longer period of general debility. I consider it very likely that the process of healing would have been accelerated if Dr Stre had put some stitches into the wound, at any rate in the two inches or so above the hip. Our voyage seemed to me very long, but I am aware that this may have been due to my feeble state of health.

Even after the healing process was properly started it was interrupted nightly by my scratching off the scab with my nails and thus bringing about a reinfection of the wound.

It is, of course, no simple matter to bandage a wound of this type securely. I often slept deeply and heavily and when I awoke the exposed part of the wound was alive with flies and tiny, light-coloured maggots or grubs. I could not see them, but I could feel them with my finger-tips and they caused intense irritation.

Jaffar Topan

Darkness fell on the second or third evening after our departure from Bari. Round about us was sea and sky, but no land.

The crew lit lanterns and hoisted them up the masts. They also hung one lantern at the stem and another at the stern of the ship.

The Barites had brought drums and pipes with them and they often danced.

Night fell. Sir John and his lieutenants bade each other good night and each went to his cabin and his bed. The *Avanti*'s quarter-deck was roped off from the rest of the ship and guarded by two Galla askaris.

The vessel's engines had a rhythm of their own that reminded one of the breathing of a very large, sleeping animal. The rhythm of the propeller was quite different. It never slept. It thrust the water away from it, it thumped. These two rhythms together kept up a dull, ponderous roar.

Men's ears are imperfect. They soon forget. A roar ceases to exist in a matter of hours.

The Barites danced on and on. They moved in waves over the deck of the ship, from rail to rail, from the stem to the place in the stern where the Gallas halted them. The people who were beating the drums or playing the pipes handled their instruments gently. They kept them low, for those who had gone to their beds must not be disturbed.

It was on this night that Dajatsj, the captain of the Gallas, decided to make himself felt. He walked so close to the musicians that they had to bend away from him and one he pushed aside with his knee. He climbed up on the hatchway of a hold.

His shirt was looped up and held fast by his belt. His hair was gleaming and there was a thin tuft of black beard on his chin. One of his soldiers gave him his shield and he fastened it to his left forearm. The shield was round and quite small. It was made of leather and adorned with the mane of a lion. There are many people who regard a lion's mane as an ornament.

The Barites went on dancing. They sang as they danced, but they sang very softly, for those who had gone to bed must not be disturbed. Their song did not rise above the noise of the ship.

I noticed that the Galla soldiers were gathering behind Dajatsj. They grouped themselves behind and in line with him, but not in front. By slow degrees more came up. Some carried torches raised aloft. The canvas covering of the hold sagged beneath their weight.

The dancing continued and things remained like this for some time.

I walked past the Barite drummers and pipe-players and stopped beside Dajatsj's feet.

'Leave them in peace, effem,' I said.

'I have not disturbed them.'

'Not yet.'

'Who are you?' he asked.

'Jaffar,' I answered. 'I am Sir John's scribe and dragoman,

but I do not know if that makes me any happier. Let the Barites go on dancing, please.'

Dajatsj's knees were on a level with my eyes. His legs were lean, but at the same time muscular. The skin on them was shiny and smooth. He must come from a country where there is no thorny undergrowth. His face too was lean, his temples were hollow, his cheek-bones sharp and his eyes emptily calm.

I had still only managed to learn a few Galla words and we therefore spoke together in English.

'They are neither Mahdists nor dervishes and their dancing is artless,' I said. 'They are dancing late, but the night is long.'

He was looking down on me, standing on the hatchway. The soldiers beside and behind him all wore white shirts, short now, for they were looped up over their belts. There were many of them, yet they were few compared to the many hundred dancing askaris and pagazis from Bari.

Dajatsj bent down, stretched out his left arm and pushed me aside. The lion's mane on his shield brushed my cheek. It felt harsh, as if each hair had on it a string of small barbs.

I went to find the captain of the ship, but I could not rouse him.

I went to Lieutenant Laronne's cabin. It was in darkness.

'Something is going to happen, sir,' I said in the dark. 'Are you awake, sir?'

He got out of bed in a hurry. He was wearing a white shirt. It reminded me of a Galla soldier's shirt as it is generally worn. The lamplight made him blink. He was thin. His cheek-bones were sharp and his temples looked hollowed out.

'Something is going to happen, sir,' I said.

We were under the quarter-deck and the propeller was thumping. You had to listen very carefully before you could hear the beat of drums or of naked heels. Laronne was wide awake.

'Who has sent you?' he said.

'No one but me, sir,' I answered, 'or possibly the captain of the Galla soldiers.'

There were two hundred Gallas aboard the *Avanti* and more than eight hundred Barites. Numbers are not always the decisive factor. When I came on deck Dajatsj's soldiers had broken the human chain of dancing Barites. In the centre of the ship was a ladder leading downwards, and to it the Barites allowed themselves to be driven.

A dozen flaming torches were held in the air. The higher a torch is held the shorter is the shadow it casts; the more torches there are the lighter it grows, for many sources of light absorb each other's shadows.

I climbed up on a superstructure the better to see what happened.

The Barites were driven towards the ladder and then down it. The Gallas threw their drums after them, but not before they had trampled on them and broken the membranes. They also broke the flutes in two and threw them after the drums. Then, stopping at nothing, they went down the ladder themselves, kicking out in all directions and swinging their spears.

Up on one of the *Avanti*'s superstructures I suddenly became aware that the Dutch captain was standing beside me. At his side stood one of the sailors holding a rifle in his hands. They watched what was happening. The Dutch captain smiled and talked rapidly, in short sentences. I do not understand his language, but I knew what he meant. He was barefoot and his chest was naked. His shirt was undone and the sleeves were cut off above the elbow.

One of my hands was resting on the rail. The captain

happened to touch it. He gave a start and made as if to turn towards me, but his movement was too hasty—perhaps he was unused to wearing no shoes—and he lost his balance so that I had to prop him up.

'Who are you?' he asked.

'Jaffar Topan, sir,' I answered.

A ship's lantern was hanging almost above me. He twisted me towards the light.

'Only Jaffar,' I said. 'Sir John's scribe and dragoman. Surely you know what a dragoman is, sir?'

'I can't allow naked lights below deck,' he said.

'Of course you can't.'

'Even paraffin lamps are dangerous.'

'Yes, sir,' I said. 'Anyone who takes a burning torch down a ladder, down below deck on a ship, is acting wrongly, whether he be a Muslim or a Copt. You should have him shot.'

The Dutch captain fell against me again. I tried to heave him off, but he took a firm grip of my arm.

'Come,' he said.

The sailor holding his rifle at the ready remained where he was. His eyes did not follow us. We descended a rope ladder. The Galla soldiers began to throw their torches into the sea. At the foot of the ladder was a passage. The Dutchman led me and I held him up. The passage was dark and so was the room on the inside of the door he opened.

He let go of my arm and I of his, and he struck a light with a match. By the light of its flame he took down a lamp from the wall, a little lamp with a glass reservoir.

'Give the lamp to me, effem,' I said.

He handed it to me and I lit the wick.

'I know more about lighting lamps than you do,' I said.

He was very excited. He pulled me along, but I had to prop him up even more than before. I carried the lamp in my left hand. We made our way through the inside of the ship until we came to a well-bolted door.

'Why must you open it?' I asked. 'You can hear. Isn't it enough to hear?'

But he was very excited, so excited that he fumbled and could not undo the bolts without my help.

The hinges of the door were so fixed that it opened into the next room. He shoved with all his might, but there were far too many struggling people pressing against it on the other side. To exert greater pressure he put his back against it and indicated again that he wanted me to help him.

'It's hopeless,' I said, 'and what is it you think you could do in there anyway?'

He was grinning with exertion, but at that moment the door opened a couple of inches. Many hands appeared in the slit. They were stronger than the Dutchman's and the door opened wide.

The captain fell backwards over the threshold and a stream of Barites poured out of the darkness and the hot smell. I got a purchase against the door-jamb and straddled across him to stop him being trampled to death. At the same time I tried to protect the lamp.

When things had grown quieter I got him on to my back with one of his arms over my shoulder, and dragged him to his cabin. He was very heavy.

After I had put him on his bed he opened his eyes, but he was unable to get up. He asked who I was and I told him my name. He was sweating profusely and all the feet that had trampled on him had made him very dirty. I dipped a face-towel in water intending to wipe him with it, but he snatched it from me and threw it at the wall. He had enough strength left in him for that.

I spread a blanket over him and left the cabin.

The dead were sewn into a sparse measure of canvas.

Weights were bound to their feet, short bits of thick cable. The dead were got ready by some of the Barite soldiers, and it was done very early in the morning. Halmadi the Syrt, the captain of the two hundred carefully selected soldiers, stood at a distance, enveloped in his worn woollen mantle, supervising them.

My nightly resting-place was hard. One of my arms was swollen and stiff. I had slept ill and was therefore awake early.

Dr Stre and Lieutenant Hansen were among those who were also early awake on this morning.

Halmadi was standing some way apart from the soldiers who were sewing and there was the same distance again between him and the two Europeans.

The smoke from the *Avanti*'s funnel drifted behind us like a black band, and another like it was formed by the smoke from the *Second*. It was one of those rare mornings when the air is chilly and everything is clammy, a morning on which even an Englishman feels cold.

Halmadi spoke to me:

'I am neither an Imam nor an undertaker. I do not even know what happened, effem. I slept until they woke me up. For what reason? "Halmadi, you must sink six dead men in the sea." "How did they die?" "You must sink them in the sea, Halmadi." It will be hot today.'

'Allah takes away a man's soul when he sleeps,' said the captain of the Barite soldiers, 'just as He takes away the soul when a man dies. But He only keeps the soul of the man whom He has destined to die. He returns the soul of the man who only sleeps. These are the Prophet's own words.'

'You must have slept soundly last night,' I said, 'but your soul was returned to you.'

'I have not counted my journeys to Mecca,' he said. 'How many times, I wonder, have I kissed Kaaba's two sacred stones? One of them is black and is called Hadjar. The other has no name.'

*

After the dead had been sunk in the sea Hansen came up to us.

'The boy, what happened to him?' he asked.

'What boy, sir?' I asked.

'The boy who stole the pearls.'

'Before we left Bari?' I asked.

'Yes.'

'Do you know, Halmadi?' I asked.

'It is a long time ago now,' answered the Barite captain. 'Is an old thief more of a thief than a young thief? Is a child less of a thief than a half-grown thief? Why do you ask?'

I said to Lieutenant Hansen:

'He says that there are children with no hands, and that we have just sunk six dead Barites in the sea.'

I wrote a letter to Sayyid Pasha.

'I have left your palace and I am on board a ship,' I wrote. 'I cannot sleep below deck for a thousand men lie there at night, and what air there is to breathe in has been breathed out many times already. On this great ship I have found a little boat, intended to carry eight rowers. It is covered with a piece of canvas, and there is room in it for my loneliness. It is like creeping into a lighted cave. I am sheltered from wind and rain, but my sleep is the sleep of a cave-dweller, for wood is as hard to lie on as a bed of stone. I am very poor now.

'You often used to speak of the sweetness of privation,' I wrote. 'Who was the sufi, the man clothed in a mantle of wool? The man who said that the poor man should hold the poverty bestowed on him by Allah dearer than the rich man the riches that Allah had given to him? What was that wise man's name? I should be glad of his woollen mantle, not for its warmth, but to make my bed softer.

'The honey of Egypt is sweet to the living, and bitter to those who are dead,' I wrote. 'To one who lives in a palace the sweetness of privation must have the bitter taste of the unobtainable.'

One evening Kingiri, the captain of No. 2 Company, sat on the deck close to my boat for eight rowers.

'Salaam,' I said. I lit a lamp and placed it between us. He was sitting with his legs outstretched, not crossed or drawn up.

'Who is Kanyi Pasha?' he asked.

'I do not know,' I answered.

Once you had seen Kingiri you could never forget him. His head was the smallest of all grown men's heads and his mouth had been enlarged by two upward-turning slits through his cheeks. You could not forget his left hand either. It had only a thumb, no fingers. Kingiri was a six-fingered man.

I cut a piece of bread in two equal parts. I ate of one part and I gave him the other. He accepted this bread and stuffed it away under his shirt and his worn leopard skin.

'I have always been on the move,' he said. 'I have never dwelt anywhere. I do not know where I was born.'

His legs were rough with the scars of many wounds and scratches. His feet were broad and the toes were widely spaced.

'Dajatsj's legs are as smooth as the legs of a sultan,' I said.

'I cannot remember the names of all the villages and towns,' he said, 'the rivers, the lakes, the harbours, the seas, the mountains, the plains, the deserts and the forests. I have always been on the move, and who Kanyi Pasha is does not trouble me.'

We sat beside each other all night. I slept much of the time and my lamp went out.

Laronne

I

While I was incapacitated by the slow-healing wound on my back Lieutenant Hansen often came to visit me in my cabin. I valued his visits as I valued the man himself. He was the youngest of us. He had the solidly built well-disciplined body of a sportsman. He was rather shy. He often blushed and he frequently averted his gaze rather than meet the eyes of the person to whom he was speaking. I was not quite certain of his age.

On one of his visits he brought up a subject which had, I felt sure, been engaging his thoughts for some time. The matter stood thus: during the preparations for the expedition, only one route for our march to the relief of Kanyi Pasha had been discussed; no alternative route had been so much as mentioned. However, by the day after our departure from Bari, it became evident that Sir John had made up his mind to find his way to our objective by a route quite other than the one we had discussed. We were going to work from east to west instead of the reverse. This change of plan involved covering more than twice the distance previously proposed, quite apart from the fact that it also prolonged our sea voyage by more than three weeks.

When Hansen did at last mention the matter in my sick-room he became very agitated, and in his agitation gave voice to several ill-considered opinions.

I remonstrated with him. 'Sir John is our leader,' I said. 'You must realize, Lieutenant Hansen, that he is perfectly at liberty to choose whatever route he considers most suitable. It's not our business, neither yours nor mine, to offer him advice.'

'Did he say anything to you about it?' he asked.

'It's certainly true that I am his second-in-command,' I answered, 'but he has not seen fit to discuss the question with me. For that matter,' I continued, 'his change of plan must have been apparent to all of us when the ship, on leaving Bari, steered south instead of west.'

'And he never said a single word!'

'Was there any reason why he should?' I asked. 'He knew that both you and I could distinguish one point of the compass from another. He realized that you were as capable as I was of calculating the significance of our change of direction.'

As I was confined to my bunk I asked Lieutenant Hansen to take down the leather brief-case in which I kept my diary and other documents of importance. It lay on a shelf over the door of the cabin.

I read part of my contract out aloud: '"I undertake to serve the leader of the expedition faithfully and loyally, and to follow him whatever route he may decide to take." Doesn't your agreement with Sir John make the same stipulation?' I asked.

'It does,' he agreed, and held out his hand for the document, but I folded it and put it back into my brief-case.

A contract is an agreement between two parties. It is nowhere stated that one such agreement must be in identically the same wording as another, contemporaneous agreement. Space is always allowed for secondary details which may diverge considerably in their content. Nor is it anywhere recommended as important or advisable that two colleagues, on a similar footing, should each know what is in the other's contract.

'But even at the time the contracts were drawn up,' said Hansen, 'Sir John knew that he was going to choose a route to the Pasha other than the one he pretended to regard as the only one suitable.'

'Your assertion is needlessly categorical, sir,' I said.

I should like to emphasize once again that Lieutenant Hansen inspired me with a feeling of liking. His lack of self-assurance could be ascribed to his youth. He was the youngest of us. He had an athlete's body and his arms were as heavy as sledge-hammers. He found it difficult to look the person he was talking to in the eye, but only the inexperienced allow such things to make them draw hackneyed conclusions. Shyness and hesitancy are often coupled with determination and loyalty in action.

Our conversation took place one afternoon. It was blowing hard and the rolling motion of the ship was having its effect upon me. It is true that I was in my bunk, but I was in a half-sitting position, resting on one elbow. The wound in my back was paining me. It was suppurating and smelt bad. There were several large, yellow blotches, as hard as scabs, on the under-sheet.

I did not know if Hansen had leave of absence, or if he had been obliged to resign in order to join the expedition. Some of the remarks he dropped did not exclude the possibility that he had returned to civilian life some time before joining. After some hesitation I asked him how old he was, but his answer was interrupted by the entrance of Dr Stre.

The latter examined my wound and then gave me a large dose of bromide, or hypobromite, dissolved in a glass of alkaline water.

'You must not eat anything salt this evening,' he said. 'One salt counteracts another. There is no better remedy for a sick or wounded man than sleep.'

He stayed quite a long time in my cabin. He stood near the door and counteracted the movements of the ship by a supple bending of his knees.

I know that Hansen answered my question when the doctor had departed, but I cannot remember the nature of his reply. I was still feverish and very tired.

II

Because of windy and rainy weather our last evening meal at sea was laid in a small saloon which was situated next door to the captain's cabin. As the ship was tossing fairly violently only soup and bread were served.

While the meal was in progress the Dutch captain suddenly rose and left the table and the saloon without uttering a word. Nothing was said about the incident until coffee, and then only in passing. After he had lit his pipe Sir John said:

'I'm sure you will all have noticed our captain's apparel which, so far as the upper part of his body is concerned, usually consists of a white, sleeveless shirt. The fact that he left the table this evening before everyone had finished and without apology may possibly have been due to sudden indisposition. On the other hand you can't expect much of a gentleman who comes to table with bare arms.'

After these introductory remarks he turned to our doctor. 'What is your opinion, Dr Stre, of bare arms in these latitudes?'

'You mean in the case of Europeans? Bare European arms?'

'Of course.'

'You want to know the medical aspect of the consequence of allowing the tropical sun to shine on unprotected white skin?' Stre lit one of his sputtering cigars, smiled, and continued:

'Your questions often surprise me, sir. At first the skin becomes red and later it takes on a browner hue. The degree of brownness varies from person to person. If one is not careful the initial reddening can be extreme and give rise to a painful condition and temporary feverishness. I do not think, however, that it was that kind of fever which obliged our Dutch friend to leave the table so hastily.'

'It may well be that I sometimes surprise you by my questions and my views,' said our leader. 'The fact of the matter is that anyone who travels a great deal is bound to notice many things which might appear surprising to, shall we say, a permanent stay-at-home.'

'I'm convinced of it,' said Dr Stre politely.

'You'll appreciate that it is one thing to display naked feet, naked arms, or even a naked torso in the temperate climate of our homelands. It's quite another matter whether you go about properly dressed or only half dressed in hot climates.'

'What you say is very interesting.'

'Generally speaking,' Sir John continued, 'there is a certain advantage to be gained by not uncovering the body, and this applies to Europe too. In the tropics nakedness can be an encumbrance, quite apart from the risks you run by exposing yourself to the sun. Under the term nakedness I here include uncovered arms and open shirts. It is of course obvious that a European can't go about barefoot.

'I'm speaking from experience,' he added. 'When he's surrounded by almost entirely naked people, the carefully dressed foreigner gains a dignity which enhances his superiority. That there is also an aesthetic and moral aspect to the matter is something of which we must all be aware.'

'I've noticed, sir,' said Dr Stre, 'that you're interested in medical problems. Among other things we once discussed the importance for health of provisioning and eating habits.'

'That problem is always present in the mind of a traveller,' replied Sir John.

'On one occasion we also had a discussion on the causes of malaria. I seem to remember that it was left unfinished.'

'The world is full of theories and theorists,' said Sir John. 'That is as it should be. I myself am a man of action. I value action and activity more highly than passive theorizing. Most theories seem to have only one function, that of giving rise to new theories of a contradictory nature. Do you follow me, Dr Stre? As a man of action I have often benefited greatly from the ideas propounded by theorists. But you have to choose from among them with care and judgment and find your own way by trial and error. You can't depend on theories.

'Few people can have been more tormented by malaria than I have,' he went on. 'One theory asserts that it is caused by miasma. Dr Koch assures us that it is brought on by bacilli. I've felt my way in the matter. There's plenty of miasma about in low-lying, waterlogged ground, protected from wind, where the air is heavy with vapours from rotting vegetable matter. I've spent weeks in areas like this without suffering from any attacks of fever. And what about Dr Koch's bacilli? Aren't they everywhere? But I don't suffer from fevers all the time.'

'Have you any theory of your own?' asked Dr Stre.

'I can induce fever,' answered Sir John. 'It's a very simple matter. I walk rapidly on a hot afternoon for a not inconsiderable distance. Wet with sweat I seat myself in the shade and allow myself to be cooled by the evening breeze. That is all that is necessary. Fever is unavoidable, especially if I should happen to be wearing flannel underwear.'

III

Our sea voyage was followed by a three-day trip up the river. The mouth of this was very wide, so wide that at first we could not see land in any direction. As time went on the coasts began to rise above the horizon and drew nearer hour by hour. We dropped anchor each night.

The *Avanti* and the *Second* steamed at reduced speed. We were visited by natives who, rather hesitantly, brought their canoes near to our ship wanting to sell us hens, fish, and fruit.

The long wound in my back healed. I never had an opportunity of seeing it, but I could feel the scar with my fingertips.

'It's wide and red,' Hansen told me. 'Under the red near the hip there's a blue-black streak.'

I asked Dr Stre about this dark streak.

'Nothing to worry about,' he said. 'I don't count you as a patient any longer.'

Sir John's comment was: 'Be thankful that you live in the present century, Lieutenant Laronne, and that you are not one of the Spartans of antiquity. Leonidas gave his doctors orders not to tend those who had been wounded in the back.'

On our fourth day we reached Port Prim. The Dutch captain fired a salute from the *Avanti*'s little cannon, a whole series of shots that no one bothered to count. Port Prim was a harbour without fortifications, so it had nothing with which to return our salute.

Jaffar Topan

In the day-time the *Avanti*'s deck swarmed with Barites and Gallas. Walking from one rail to another was like forcing your way across a market-place. During the hottest hours of the day they sought what shade there was, and also fastened up mats or pieces of cloth wherever they could. These mats and bits of cloth were taken down each evening by their owners. Otherwise they might have been stolen or blown into the sea by a sudden gust of wind.

The Galla soldiers regarded the forward part of the ship as their own, and turned away any Barite who ventured near it. They themselves, however, moved about over the whole ship, right up to the part in the stern reserved for Sir John.

At night, when everyone had gone to bed, the deck looked desolate. It was slippery and dirty and strewn with as much rubbish as a market square. Each morning, at sunrise, it was swilled clean with sea-water.

On yet another night Kingiri, the six-fingered captain of the boat-bearers, came to my canvas-covered boat for eight rowers. He sat down on the deck close to it. I lit my lamp and placed it between us. He cut a dried fruit in two halves and gave me one.

'I have never dwelt anywhere,' he said. 'I have always been a traveller.'

'There are whole peoples who live by owning sheep, or goats, or camels,' I answered, 'and such people are always journeying to another place.'

'Where do you live?' he asked.

'I once lived in a palace,' I answered. 'You know who Sayyid Bey is? Now I live here,' I said, and knocked my eight-oared boat with the back of my head. 'I have always lived somewhere.'

'Soon you will not always have lived somewhere,' he said. Then he walked forward and I followed him with my lamp.

It was late and very quiet. A faint sound of voices came from the captain's bridge, that was all. He walked ahead of me and down the ladder to the bowels of the ship. It was like sinking into a well of hot, rancid smells.

'Wait, effem,' I said, and Kingiri paused at the foot of the ladder and stood there for some time.

The paraffin lamps that hung from the ceiling were burning low, and my lamp was needed. The sleepers were lying so close to each other that only with difficulty could you put down your foot without touching an arm, a leg, or a back.

There were three sleeping-areas divided by short gangways. Most of the sleepers lay on their sides with their knees drawn up. The gangways between the areas were so narrow that those whose places were near them had to sleep sitting up. Two nursing mothers looked at us, but without curiosity. Many of the sleepers had made their belongings into small bundles, which they had fastened firmly to one arm. Down the iron outer sides of the ship ran little streams of moisture.

Kingiri spread out his mat between two of his subordinates. 'I have always been on the move,' he said. 'If you travel by boat you do not have to walk.'

I left him but found it difficult to make my way back to the ladder. Kingiri must have been able to detect a path between those sleeping Barites that my eyes could not find.

We had to keep ourselves in food during our voyage, but each of us was given a daily ration of water from the ship's tanks. For the first part of the time the Barites lived in plenty, after that there was want.

Halmadi, the captain of the askaris, had brought with him quite a large supply of rice and wheat, which he guarded carefully, and later on sold to those without provisions. He had once been a Barite merchant's slave, and he was now the widower of the merchant's widow.

'I was once going to be a merchant myself,' I told him.

'I am no merchant,' he answered. 'Nevertheless, Allah has bestowed on me a small measure of forethought, and my own wits have taught me to know the Barites. My prices are not those of a merchant. I am merely obeying the commands of the Koran to help those in need.'

The Barites put new membranes on the drums the Galla soldiers had ruined and they cut new pipes. They resumed their dancing and nothing further happened.

'You are allowing them to dance,' I said to Dajatsj.

'And why should they not be allowed to dance?' said the captain of the Gallas.

We left the sea and we journeyed up a river. The heat grew very great; you could burn your hand by laying it on the *Avanti*'s deck.

The rattle of the anchor-cables was a strange and unfamiliar sound. Steam hissed from the funnels of the ship, the engines and the propeller stopped, and this unwonted silence made my head feel empty.

Laronne

I

Soon after the *Avanti* and the *Second* dropped anchor we were rowed ashore and welcomed by the European population of Port Prim—Belgian, Dutch, French, English, and German. This enumeration may suggest a town of some importance, but such was not the case. The total number of Europeans in the place was forty at the outside.

Port Prim lay on a tongue of land round which the river wound. This tongue was formed by a fairly high ridge, which had been cleared of undergrowth and most of its trees. About a dozen trees had been left and, in their new state of isolation, these had grown tall and spread out their branches, forming gigantic shady parasols.

The houses belonging to the Europeans were situated on the crown of the ridge. They were built of whitewashed brick, placed at an agreeable distance from each other, and surrounded by lawns, hedges, and flowering shrubs. Port Prim had the air of being a pleasant place. It was quite an important port, not least for the export of ivory.

Down by the primitive quay were two long rows of large warehouses, roofed with leaves. Their walling was wide-spaced, like lattice-work, and its thin planks had dried and warped so that they were twisted and bulging.

The native population lived on the slopes of the ridge in huts skilfully built of reeds and mud. They had cultivated such parts of the shore as were not used as wharves and, in addition, about an acre of ground to the north of the European houses on the ridge.

Sir John was accommodated in the largest house in Port Prim. The owner was a Dutch merchant, a clean-shaven and very courteous gentleman, who was always dressed in a spotless white suit. He was the British Consul, but had besides a number of other consular commissions. He had placed his entire house at Sir John's disposal. It was furnished in a manner that indicated both good taste and a liking for comfort. He had many native servants, and was assisted in his work by an English clerk. A number of things led me to conclude that Sir John and this Dutchman had known one another for a long time.

During the short time we spent in Port Prim he retired early. He always did so very discreetly. He would suddenly appear in the doorway, smile kindly, bow and leave us without any appearance of haste.

We took our meals in an outdoor room, a sort of veranda, with a wooden floor, a tiled roof, and walls of close-woven netting. This did not obstruct our view but it protected us from flying insects and yet allowed the breeze to enter almost unhindered.

II

In Port Prim two episodes occurred of a not altogether pleasant nature. Lodging had been arranged for Stre, Hansen, Smitt, and myself in the house of the Dutch merchant's nearest neighbour, but only two rooms were put at our disposal.

Dr Stre announced that he could not accept this arrangement, and claimed the right to have a room to himself.

'You must not take this to mean disapproval of you, gentlemen,' he said, 'or of whichever one of you had turned out to be my stable-companion. It is purely a question of a deep-seated habit,' he said, addressing Sir John, 'and one which I am not prepared to relinquish.'

Our leader regarded him very calmly.

'You surprise me, Dr Stre,' he said.

To which Stre replied:

'I should like to remind you, sir, of what you yourself once said about the perils of displaying bare feet and arms, even though I did not entirely agree with all the views expressed on that occasion.'

Sir John did not allow himself to be drawn in further exchanges with Stre.

With the help of the Dutch merchant he secured another room in a house situated rather further away, which belonged to the representative of a German company.

The other episode was also in the nature of an altercation, but it undoubtedly had a much more serious background.

The Dutch merchant treated us to an excellent dinner by way of welcome. After it we sat down in his library, but not before our host had asked us to excuse the noticeable, but not offensive, smell of ammonia and alcohol. These, he informed us, were necessary ingredients in the tincture used to protect paper and leather bindings from the attacks of insects and small rodents.

In answer to our host's questions Sir John gave him an account of how men and materials were to be transported by boat up the river to Fort John, from which place the expedition would march eastwards to the region in which—according to the latest reports—Kanyi Pasha now was.

The Dutchman fetched a rolled-up map which he spread out on his reading-table and held open with four lead weights.

'You understand,' he said, turning chiefly to Dr Stre and myself, 'that though I reside in Port Prim and shall soon have lived here for half a lifetime, my first-hand knowledge of the country further inland is in the strictest sense of the word rudimentary. I have made a number of short trips by boat, that is all. My health has not permitted me to undertake any extensive excursions. This, however, does not diminish my interest in the expedition, or the route Sir John is planning to follow.'

'We too,' said Lieutenant Hansen, 'are very interested in the route Sir John intends to follow.'

'The trip up the river to Fort John,' our host continued, 'is a comparatively trivial matter. The distance to be covered is admittedly considerable, but of recent years river-boat traffic has been greatly developed, and it is this that has made possible the expansion of Port Prim as a port.

'On the other hand, I am greatly impressed by your daring, Sir John, in combining your expedition for the relief of Kanyi Pasha with a march through a very extensive and practically unexplored region.'

After saying this he dropped the subject and turned to the question of what the chances were that Port Prim would develop into a still more important trading-station and port. This was, of course, a matter he had very much at heart and one in which we could see that Sir John was also deeply interested.

Some hours later the Dutchman retired, but not before he had put out refreshments and given us the kindest assurances that his library was at our disposal.

Sir John immediately took up the question of the actual duties we should be expected to perform.

'The unloading of the *Avanti* and the *Second* must start tomorrow,' he said.

I asked if it would not be better to await the arrival of the river-boats, so that our stores could be transferred directly to them.

'My agreement with the shipowners contains a clause in which it is stipulated that the ships shall leave Port Prim as soon as possible.'

'Unloading the ships before the arrival of the river-boats will involve a lot of extra work, sir,' I said.

'I'm aware of that fact.'

'When can we expect the river-boats?'

'In a few days, or in a week,' he answered. 'For that matter,' he added, filling and lighting his pipe, 'for that matter only three boats will be available to us, and they are too small to allow us to transport all our men and all our supplies at one time.'

'That sounds like faulty organization,' said Hansen, rising from his seat and taking a few hasty steps across the floor.

'It's no part of your duties, Lieutenant Hansen, to comment upon my talents as an organizer,' replied Sir John.

'You can't deprive me of the right to my own opinion.'

'One can keep one's own opinions to oneself,' I remarked.

'I don't think I need your assistance, Lieutenant Laronne,' said Sir John, and to Hansen: 'May I suggest that you sit down again? As it is you appear altogether too agitated.'

He spoke throughout with unruffled calm. His voice was harsh and slightly petulant. Words and sentences fell from his lips like little streams of gravel, to avail oneself of one of Hansen's modes of expression.

As I have already emphasized, Hansen, the youngest of us, was a rather shy man, who blushed readily and often avoided meeting the eyes of the person to whom he was speaking. His outburst to Sir John was not the blunt comment of a self-assured man, but rather a symptom of the temporary lack of self-control which one sometimes observes in shy, rather insecure young persons.

III

The Dutch merchant complained on one occasion about the shaky state of his health, and his perpetual tiredness which he attributed to dysentery and abscesses on his liver.

There was no doctor in Port Prim and I know that Dr Stre offered his services. I believe I am right in saying that they were refused.

IV

In the course of four arduous days I accomplished the unloading of the *Avanti* and the *Second.* Both ships drew too much water for it to be possible for them to lie up alongside the primitive quay, and consequently the unloading could only be carried out with a great deal of help from rowers, small boats, and lighters. The last were so improvised that they might just as well have been called rafts.

I should have preferred to warehouse our stores, but we were obliged to pile them up in the open, barely covered by borrowed tarpaulins. For practical reasons we made them into two stacks. One was guarded by Gallas. The Barite askaris were put in charge of the other.

The unloading was a difficult business, especially the work of shifting the goods from the lighters on to dry land. The quay, as I said before, was a very primitive construction. There were no cranes and only one flight of steps, the woodwork of which was rotten and unsafe. If the largest of the lighters was heavily laden the porters often had to wade to the shore through water up to their hips.

Hansen remarked:

'I could give our merchant friend the Consul a number of hints on certain necessary provisions that would have to be made before Port Prim could be developed as an important trading-station.'

And Smitt replied:

'It is no part of your duties, Lieutenant Hansen, to express your opinion on technical matters connected with ports.'

No local labour was recruited for the unloading apart from a small number of rowers. Our own men were quite sufficient, and these displayed a healthy appetite for work after their enforced immobility during the voyage.

The natives of Port Prim were inquisitive and importunate. They swarmed all over our section of the harbour and circled round our boats and lighters in their canoes.

A number of petty thefts occurred, and one morning the Gallas opened fire on a heavily laden canoe that was trying to escape up river. As it drifted away it was intercepted and brought ashore by other canoes. Of the crew two were dead and a third severely wounded. The rest had escaped by jumping into the water.

The two who were dead had both been hit in the head. The wounded man had been hit by a single bullet which had passed through the upper part of his left arm and entered his chest. I had him carried ashore, but he died before Dr Stre managed to arrive on the scene.

The behaviour of the natives amazed me. After they had silently emptied the canoe of its stolen cargo and handed the goods over to us, they carried the dead man back on board and laid him besides his two comrades. They then pushed the canoe out into the river and let it drift away with the current. The tide was ebbing and the canoe very soon disappeared from our sight.

Hansen and Smitt gave me useful help while we were unloading the ships. One man had to stay on board and two men were essential for the effective supervision of the quayside, with its valuable and ever-growing stacks of goods.

At his own request Smitt assisted me ashore. It was decidedly shadier there than on board the *Avanti* or the *Second.* Smitt had the fairest skin and the lightest-coloured eyes of any of us, and during the voyage the sun had caused him a certain amount of trouble. Among other things it had given rise to a mild inflammation of the eyes, for which he had been treated by Dr Stre.

'Perhaps you should also consult our leader,' the doctor had said. 'He has had considerable experience of matters appertaining to this subject.'

During the time we spent in Port Prim I really only saw Dr Stre at mealtimes. He stayed indoors most of the time and only came down to the harbour once; namely, on the occasion when he arrived too late to render aid to the native who had been severely wounded by the Gallas. Hansen asserted that he was afraid of snakes.

Sir John handed over all responsibility for the unloading to me, and only paid us one hasty visit of inspection. His residence, however, bore no resemblance to a sanatorium or rest-home. He was in a state of feverish activity for the greater part of the day. I know that almost two hundred letters and other documents were awaiting him when we arrived at Port Prim. I know that the mail-boat which called at the port some days later brought with her a passable number of letters and documents of one sort or another. I know too that, in spite of the reliable financiers and guarantors behind the expedition, Sir John had some acute monetary difficulties which he only succeeded in overcoming by persuading the leading merchants and business agents in Port Prim to provide him with funds, which he had to borrow at a high rate of interest.

Jaffar Topan

The harbour at Port Prim was shallow. The ships anchored some distance from the quay and both the Barites and the Gallas were rowed ashore in small boats.

The Barites were singing. Many grew impatient and could not wait their turn, but jumped into the water and swam ashore or hung on to the fully laden boats.

I turned to Dajatsj:

'Why do the Galla soldiers never sing?' I asked.

'Maybe you will hear us sing one day,' he answered.

Many people had been ill on the voyage, but they forgot about it when they once more stood on dry land. Others felt ill for the first time when they came ashore. They felt bewildered and sick because there was no motion, and walked with their legs wide apart.

The Barites were allotted quarters in a large warehouse. There was not room in it for all of them and many built themselves simple shelters of bits of plank and leaves against the warehouse walls. Many did not take the trouble to do this, but slept under the open sky, wrapped in their mats.

The Gallas were quartered in a low, dilapidated building. It was narrow and very long. The floor was of earth trampled hard as stone, and there were only two entrances, one very small and the other somewhat larger. I have once seen a ropery and I think that perhaps this building had once been such a place.

From the moment we landed it was Sir John's business to keep us all in provisions and Port Prim was a town where there were many things to eat: maize, plantains, figs, honey, and cassava. Cassava is a bread made of manioc, and manioc is also called arrowroot.

Our provisions were dealt out to us in the mornings. The leader of each company was given the ration for his company and with the help of his foremen had to see to it that each man got his share. In addition, anyone who wanted could buy hens, eggs, molasses, grapes, earth-nuts, fish, rice, sweet corn, dates, turtles, and coconuts, at a low price. Port Prim was in truth a place of much food.

I bought myself a little tent from the son of a Belgian merchant.

'What do you want a tent for?' he asked.

'The nights in Port Prim are damp,' I answered. 'Is it because of the wind from the sea?'

'But you are going on from here,' he said.

'Kingiri says that it often rains when one is on a journey. Perhaps you don't know who Kingiri is, but if you ever see him you will not forget him, even if you don't know that it is Kingiri whom you see. How much does the tent cost?'

The Belgian merchant's son named his price partly in pounds and partly in dollars. I converted the sum into Maria Theresa dollars and paid him in this coinage. He became embarrassed and unsure of himself and accepted what I gave him.

I pitched my tent not far from the house in which Sir John was living; was I not his scribe and dragoman? Said came to visit me. It was evening and he was guided by my lamp.

'I should like to stay here,' he said. 'The days are warm and the nights are balmy. Everything that is sown is also harvested. The earth is soft, there is never a drought here.'

'There are better places still,' I answered. 'There are better places never endingly. Otherwise why should there be so many travellers?'

'I have never before seen so many or such large flowers, he said. 'Their perfume is everywhere. There is more honey here than you can collect. You can even bake bread here of roots.'

'This morning the Galla soldiers shot three thieves.'

'The dates grow wild and the river is full of fish. Jaffar! The largest of the canoes can carry twenty men with paddles.'

'The three dead men were pushed out on the river. Their honour was thrown to the winds, their bodies to the fishes,' I said. 'A journey once began should not be interrupted. The nights in Port Prim are damp rather than balmy. My tent is large enough for you too.'

Said, the boy from Amman, fetched his mat, rolled himself in it, and slept.

We travelled up the river in three small steamers. They were broad in the beam, drew little water, and were very easy to manœuvre. Two were driven by paddles, the third had a propeller. The larger of the paddle-steamers towed a little fleet of canoes. All three steamers were small.

Sir John's boat was the first to leave Port Prim. Smitt and Dr Stre were on board and also the greater number of the Galla soldiers. Sir John had a trumpet sounded when the boat left the quay. A flag was hoisted and the Gallas fired a volley into the air. We did not see them again until we reached the trading-station that is called Fort John.

It took us a long time to travel up the river. The two

remaining boats, the one driven by a propeller and the larger of the paddle-steamers, did short trips up and down, none lasting longer than half a day. A thousand men had to be transported and the boats were far too small. The two together and the canoes towed by one of them could not carry more than three hundred men at the most.

I was going with Laronne, Sir John's vakeel. He still found it hard to understand the Barite dialects.

We left Port Prim in the morning, and before the sun was at its height our passengers were set ashore. We then returned to our starting-point, loaded the boat anew and reached the camping-place at sunset. The other boat had gone on further up the river. It returned to Port Prim so late that it could not make the next trip until the following day. That is how we made the journey to Fort John. The boats travelled up and down the river. They met and passed each other. The camping-places were endless, and each day the one furthest ahead was moved another half day's journey up river.

'To travel is a form of piety,' I said to Laronne. 'Someone had written these words and Sayyid Bey has spoken them. Our way of travelling is a work of art. Perhaps piety too is an art. Sayyid Bey is the Sultan's eldest son.'

'Which Sultan?' he asked.

'The Sultan of Bari, effendim,' I answered 'Thanks to the way in which we travel, up and down, to and fro, I think our piety must be increased at least threefold.'

We returned to Port Prim three times. Our last departure was to have taken place in the morning. Laronne came down to the quay with the British Consul beside him. He was wearing a new white suit that he had bought from a tailor of Arabic origin in Port Prim.

We were ready to leave. Steam was up and it was full daylight.

'Sir,' I said, 'the boat is crowded but fifteen men are missing. They will be left behind here since we are not going to return.'

I showed him the list I had of the men, one of the copies I had made from Sir John's roll.

'I am a scribe,' I said, 'but I can also count, and I am very careful. I was once going to be a merchant. Do you want to know their names? Eleven of them belong to No. 2 Company, three to No. 7, the last is a Galla. Names are difficult to translate.

'You yourself, effendim,' I said, 'and Sir John, have said that I must watch out that no one is left behind. Many people travelled with the other boat, but I am very careful.'

Our departure was delayed by half a day. Taking with him ten Gallas Laronne searched the whole of Port Prim. They were followed by an ever-increasing troop of natives, numbering in the end several hundred.

In the course of the search Laronne crossed a field newly sown with maize or dhurra. For this he was held up by the natives, who demanded compensation for the damage that had been done.

'They are not thinking so much of your footsteps and those of the Galla soldiers,' I said, 'but, as you can see for yourself, sir, they themselves are a considerable body, and they have followed you and trampled a wide road through the field.'

'I did not ask them to follow me.'

'All the same they think you are to blame,' I said.

'I never asked them to trample a road where no road should be.'

'But they think that but for you no one would have trampled on the field. The world is a big place. There are many peoples and many languages. One language is not the same as another, effendim, and people think as they speak.

The field has been newly sown, either with maize or with dhurra.'

Laronne never found any of the missing men.

Sometimes the river was narrow, sometimes it was wide. We seldom saw any banks. The forest was a green wall that stretched right out into the river. The roots of the outermost trees often seemed to have changed direction and to be reaching upwards, as if they hoped to find in the air the firm footing that the shifting river-bottom could not give them.

Where there were banks there were also villages, but all of them were desolate and deserted. We spent our nights in such villages. The men piloting the boats knew where they were to be found.

'Halmadi the Syrt knows all the suras as well as you do,' I wrote in a letter to Sayyid Bey. 'He complained bitterly about the Barites when we reached the harbour of Port Prim. "So long as they are on board ship," he said, "they call upon Allah, and worship Him sincerely; but once Allah has brought them ashore they repudiate His gifts." Is not all this to be found in the sura called The Spider? Is not the spider's dwelling the most fragile of all dwellings? I have but a poor memory, Sayyid.

'Halmadi ought to complain even more now,' I wrote, 'for, even if we are now on board a vessel, albeit a small one, I have seen no Muslim who either invokes or worships.

'The water is calm. They are well off for food, for which they need pay nothing. They are all well rested and no longer in need of sleep. They make up new songs, and they sing as if they were children. They shade themselves from the sun with large leaves and they splash each other with water like children at play.

'Before the days of the Prophet perhaps there was only sea or desert,' I wrote. 'Do you think he ever saw a river large enough to carry a vessel? I know that on the island of Bari there are no rivers.

'The days are very hot and the nights humidly warm.'

The third steamer, the one in which Sir John had left Port Prim, returned down the river several times to ferry up supplies. When that was done she helped to transport the men.

The boats often went aground in spite of their pilots' ability. We often ran out of dry wood. The boiler of the big paddle-steamer, Laronne's boat, went wrong, its power began to fail, and the men in the canoes it was towing had to help out with their paddles when the river was narrow.

It was very difficult to keep track of what was happening. Where was the camp furthest down the river? Which boat ought to go to it? Where was the camp furthest up the river? Which boat ought to pass it and how much further up should it travel?

Our boat, Laronne's boat, turned in at one of the deserted villages which were our nightly camping places. It lay on a promontory. The banks were steep and we glided in under the branches of trees. Tall reeds were pushed aside and broken. A swarm of birds rose up and the prow of the boat gently embedded itself in the mould of the steep bank.

The promontory was narrow. The deserted village, formed of two circles lying close together, stretched across it like the figure of an Arabic eight.

The village was far too small. Those first ashore laid claim to the nearest of the huts, those who followed them had to take the huts further away. The village was far too small and those who went ashore last began to fight those who had got there before them. They were all Barites.

The fighting grew fierce. Not only was the village small, but the huts lay close together. They were built of reeds and mud and were low and slightly tapering. Such a hut could give protection against torrential rain, but if a Barite braced himself against it or struck it as he fell it toppled over.

Laronne climbed up on a fallen tree. Two of the Gallas, Sjimba, the captain of the bearers, and one of his foremen, fired shots into the air until the fighting ceased.

Laronne gave orders that the men should be divided into equal groups and that one should spend the night in the lower part of the village, the other in the upper. He said that he would not tolerate further fighting. He spoke very fast, using many words, and I interpreted what he said.

While the men were being divided into groups one of the Barites failed to get out of the way in time. Laronne's rattan switch caught him round the neck. He fell backwards, and in doing so twisted over so that he lay with his back uppermost. His clothes had been torn to ribbons in the fight and he was almost naked.

Laronne, the vakeel, paused and then dealt him further blows. He hit very hard. His arm was stretched out taut and he rose on his toes so that his whole body followed the movement of his arm. He hit very skilfully too. As the cane touched the man's body he drew it swiftly towards him and by this means tore asunder the skin that had not been broken by the blow itself.

When he had done he put the camp in Sjimba's charge. He and I and the Galla soldiers went aboard the boat to return down river.

This happened in the middle of the day.

While we were journeying up and down the river Laronne was always accompanied by ten or eleven Gallas. Their language was easy to learn. It had few words and these, as a rule, were short. They used these few words sparingly. Taciturnity is a Galla virtue.

The foreman of the ten or eleven soldiers was called Five Pounds. I asked why he was called by this name.

'It happened long ago,' he answered.

'What were you called before?'

'I had another name.'

'I too have had another name,' I said.

The Gallas always sought the shade if they could find any. They sweated profusely and they drank great quantities of water.

The river was muddy but it tasted cool and fresh.

Said, the boy from Amman, had gone with Sir John when the latter left Port Prim. I did not see him again until after our arrival at the trading-station they call Fort John.

At this place the river had broadened out into a lake. It was so wide that one could not always see from one bank to the other. The forest had receded, and the land around the lake was a slightly undulating plain, cultivated in places, but otherwise overgrown by tall grass, with isolated trees or groves of trees here and there.

Fort John was a trading-station. It was not a town any more than Port Prim. The houses were small and thinly scattered over a large area. Streets were unnecessary. The ground was firm and hard, no grass grew where men walked, and there was not so much as the trace of a wheel-track.

The shore of the lake was shallow so they had built a long jetty out of wood.

A strong head wind was blowing when our boat, the first, reached the station. The waves were short and athwart us. At times the paddle-wheel caught the crest of a wave and threw cascades of water over the stern deck. The men in the canoes we were towing had to lend a hand with their paddles.

Laronne had hoisted a flag in the bows. A troop of Gallas fired a welcoming volley from the jetty. Smitt was standing at the head of the line, waving. Sir John and Dr Stre were watching us through binoculars from a low hill some hundred feet behind the place where the jetty began.

Grass, bushes, trees and branches were bending in the wind which was laden with a strange, heavy perfume. Small herds of sheep moved restlessly about among the houses. There were plenty of hens, and goats. Cows were ruminating calmly. They had sharp horns and distended udders.

Said helped me to pitch my tent in a little plantation of young palm trees. We tied it between two trees that had withered. The leaves had fallen and the trunks were so rigid that the wind could not bend them. The surrounding palm trees gave us shelter. I fastened the tent-cloth to the ground and Said made a floor of grasses.

When we had finished he went away, but returned at nightfall with his mat and his other belongings. These were so few that they could all be kept in a little leather bag.

'Here I am!' he exclaimed, saluting me as warmly as if we were now meeting again for the first time.

I had a little copper pan. In it Said cooked two fish and a measure of rice over a fire I had lit with matches from the palace in Bari.

Laronne

I

At our very first meeting after my arrival at Fort John, Sir John pointed out how very important it was that the expedition should proceed on its way as soon as possible. He did not display any outward signs of uneasiness, but re-emphasized on several occasions the urgency of a speedy departure.

I asked if by any chance he had had further news of Kanyi Pasha, and if so, whether this had indicated that the Pasha's situation had deteriorated. He replied in the negative and added:

'How could I have obtained such news? Suppose, Lieutenant Laronne, that the Pasha had written me a letter three months ago. When do you think that letter would reach me? Three months after I had actually met him, at the earliest.

'Our expedition has borne the stamp of urgency,' he continued, 'from the moment it became known that the Pasha and his men were in difficulties, and from the moment it became clear that a relief expedition could be financed. You cannot know anything of the haste with which the preparations were made. It is possible that you noticed my eagerness in Bari. The duration of our journey by sea was determined by the capacity of our ship's engines. But from now onwards, the necessity for haste is something that directly affects each one of us.'

Sir John had taken up his quarters in the main office building of the station, a fairly small place that looked like a bungalow—to use an Indian word. Nevertheless he had been able to make himself reasonably comfortable, as the man in charge of the station, a Polish engineer of German origin, had been dismissed some months previously on the ground that he was suffering from a lingering fever. The man who was temporarily acting as his substitute already had a residence of his own.

This acting head of the station was also an engineer. By nationality he was an Italian from Milan and very young. He struck me as being rather too bookish. The impression he produced was one of timidity and it was difficult to understand how he came to be in Fort John.

The name Fort John would seem to imply that the place was fortified in one way or another, but such was not the case. Fort John was purely a trading-station, nothing more. It had been established where it was because the land on which it was built was dry and healthy, because the large lake provided excellent means of communication with a considerable area, and because the native tribe of the region, the Ajantis, had not adopted a hostile or uncooperative attitude.

The station had grown rapidly. Some Ajantis had settled there, cultivated the ground, and built themselves houses of sun-dried mud. Point John, or something like it, would perhaps have been a more suitable name than Fort John.

II

At our first evening meal together in Fort John our leader brought up the question of our future journey to the place where Kanyi Pasha was probably to be found. Hansen did not participate in the meal or in the discussion. His river-boat had not yet arrived at the station.

Sir John dealt in particular with the problems connected with the transport of the necessities destined for the Pasha and of our own supplies. I suddenly became aware that he was sitting turned towards me and that it was to me in particular that he was addressing his remarks.

'A relief expedition,' he said, 'is primarily a question of the weight to be carried and the number and capacity of the bearers available.'

'I find myself somewhat at sea in this matter, sir,' I said. 'I'm an infantry man, I'm not an *officier du train*.'

'No need to be so cautious and modest, Lieutenant Laronne,' said Dr Stre. 'This isn't a question of a military campaign, or is it?'

'You're probably right, Dr Stre,' I replied. 'What has taken place so far would appear to be more in the nature of a naval operation, don't you agree?'

Stre was holding one of his cigars between his fingers, but he did not put it into his mouth until Said, Sir John's attendant, had poured out a second cup of coffee, and our leader had filled and lit his pipe.

'My climatological knowledge is strictly limited,' Stre went on, 'likewise my acquaintance with the subject of meteorology. Nevertheless, I would venture the surmise that our journey here from the coast has been favoured by abnormally good weather conditions. As you must have observed, Lieutenant Laronne, it has only rained a couple of times. Previous experience tells me that the longer abnormal conditions prevail, the less likely they are to continue.'

I bent forward and lit his cigar.

'I believe, sir,' he added, 'that we must now expect rainfall of such proportions that our resumed journey will continue, at least for a month or two, to retain the character of a naval expedition.'

Sir John interrupted our exchanges, and asked me to present myself at his residence as soon as I awoke the following morning.

Just before I went to bed Smitt came to my room. We were both living in the annex belonging to the main office, a building that had been put up especially for the accommodation of casual visitors. He stopped just inside the door, but closed it behind him.

'Doesn't Dr Stre annoy you?' he asked.

'I'm sure he's a capable doctor,' I answered. 'He's young enough to keep up with modern developments, and old enough to have had time to accumulate a considerable body of experience.'

'He ought to know better than to behave as he does.'

'Possibly he should,' I answered.

Smitt remained standing by the door. His smile was pleasant and his eyes were candid.

'May I ask you one more question?' he asked.

'Of course,' I answered.

'Have you made up your mind about Sir John?'

'Your question is put in very general terms, Lieutenant Smitt,' I said.

'You're right, sir,' he said. 'You don't really want to discuss him, do you?'

'I don't,' I answered.

'You are always very correct, Lieutenant Laronne,' he said, and wishing me a polite good night, he departed.

III

I presented myself at the main office at sunrise. Kingiri, the captain of No. 2 Company, and about ten of his men were sitting on the grass by the steps.

The pagazis of No. 2 Company were going to carry the supplies destined for Kanyi Pasha, and they were therefore called porters, to distinguish them from the ordinary bearers.

Looking at Kingiri gave one an odd sensation. By slitting open his cheeks, both corners of his mouth had been extended by about an inch. I had previously encountered native tribes whose custom it was to disfigure the mouth by sticking pieces of polished wood through the lips. I had seen natives whose heads had been severely deformed by being tightly bound at birth. There are regions where convention demands that practically every inch of the body must be covered with brightly coloured tattooing in relief, and it is by no means unusual to find ears and noses, for instance, ornamented by being pierced with pieces of horn or metal. In itself the extension of the mouth that Kingiri had suffered was a trifling matter. But the effect it produced was extraordinarily striking, and he made a deep impression on everyone who saw him.

The seated men greeted me with a muttered salaam as I walked past them and into the bungalow-like building.

I had expected to find Sir John indoors, perhaps not yet fully awake, but he entered almost immediately after me by the same door. My first sight of him was of a silhouette against the morning sunshine, in high boots, tight breeches, and a long coat with shoulders that the tailor had padded out to produce a broad, horizontal effect.

'Good morning, Lieutenant Laronne,' he said, and laid aside his black stick.

You might easily have thought that he had not slept at all

during the night, that he had set out on his walk in the evening, after we had parted, and that this nocturnal promenade had only been terminated by the coming of dawn. His boots, the knees of his breeches, and the cuffs of his coat, were all damp with dew and moisture.

Said, Sir John's attendant, served coffee, butter, marmalade and biscuits, and we ate our breakfast in silence. Our simple meal was remarkable in that we two were the only people at it. Smitt and Stre were still in bed, and Hansen had not yet arrived at Fort John.

Kingiri and his men waited patiently on the grass outside the building.

The heaped-up stock of necessities that were to be conveyed to Kanyi Pasha were rapidly converted into man-loads under the direction of Sir John and Kingiri. The major part of what had to be carried consisted of rifles and ammunition.

The loads were made up in the following way. Two rifles were laid on a piece of canvas with the barrels close together and the butts approximately two feet apart. A number of packets of ammunition were laid between the rifles, the canvas was wrapped round them and tied securely with string. The package was then made rigid with the help of ten slender bamboo poles, round which another piece of canvas was firmly lashed. The load when finished was stiff, and conical in shape.

It had to be carried with the point to the front and could easily be shifted from one shoulder to the other without the porter having to pause in his tracks. The canvas gave protection against rain and the load could be carelessly thrown to the ground without endangering the contents.

The remaining goods intended for Kanyi Pasha were packed in identically the same way. All the loads were conical in shape and all had the same protective covering of bamboo poles and canvas. The only exceptions were four cases of ammunition. Kingiri thought it best not to open them, but to have them lashed to a pole and carried between two porters.

The rifles in the loads were Sniders. The four cases, however, contained ammunition for Remingtons.

'It may be that the cases of ammunition are useless loads,' said Sir John. 'According to our most reliable source of information the Pasha's men are armed with Remingtons, and if that is the case all will be well. Certain other reports, however, seem to indicate that the Vetterli rifle is the one most in use.'

'That would be unfortunate, sir,' I said.

'I observed on a previous occasion that as a professional soldier you are well informed on the subject,' said Sir John. 'It is therefore probably quite unnecessary to point out that the Vetterli, in spite of the fact that it is generally regarded as an Italian weapon, is really manufactured in Switzerland, and is the predecessor of the American Winchester.'

Kingiri's men worked rapidly and efficiently. In less than two days they had converted into loads not only the goods intended for the Pasha, but also the entire stock of supplies belonging to the expedition.

A man's load should weigh between seventy-two and seventy-four pounds in English weight. In this instance, however, the measurement of weight used was a frasilah and a man's load equalled two frasilahs. I should perhaps add by way of clarification that two frasilahs correspond approximately to sixty-six pounds.

In matters of weight it is often very difficult—not to say impossible—to compare small heavy objects with those that are light but bulky. Naturally we could not always make use of such weighing-machines as were available in the station. That would have been a far too meticulous and time-wasting procedure. Moreover, it proved to be entirely unnecessary.

Kingiri, the captain of the porters, knew not only how a load should be packed, and how much it ought to weigh, he could also estimate the exact weight of an object or a package by testing it in his hand. His right arm was a steelyard whose trustworthiness never needed to be questioned.

In spite of his origin Kingiri was a person who commanded respect. He listened attentively when he was addressed. He was obeyed when he, in his turn, issued orders to his men. He behaved with gravity and determination. He had about him an air of dignity which was in no way diminished by his bare legs and feet and his extremely scanty and somewhat absurd clothing, which consisted of a dirty loin-cloth and a tattered leopard skin.

IV

'An expedition of this kind,' said Sir John at our evening meal on the third day after my arrival at Fort John, 'is largely a question of figures, a question of computations, calculations, and the weighing up of alternatives.'

'You mentioned this, sir,' said Dr Stre, 'while we were still lying at anchor in Bari harbour.'

'I was not thinking of entering into the subject in detail,' replied out leader. 'I was only going to point out a few things which it may be valuable for you to know.

'Let's take as our starting-point our company of porters, which numbers two hundred and fifty men,' he continued. 'Let's pause for a moment to consider this one company, which is, in fact, the very heart of the expedition. We are going to cross a tract of country very deficient in the means of subsistence. I can't count upon being able, day by day, to procure for you the provisions you will require. When we arrive at places where there is food to be bought, or obtained by other means, it will be necessary for us to add as much as possible to our stocks, to see to it that we provide ourselves with food for as many days as we can. We shall never know when we are again likely to come across a village capable of supplying us with further provisions.'

'May I interject a question, Sir John?' asked Dr Stre.

'What is your question?'

'You spoke of provisions that could be bought, but also those obtained by other means. What exactly do you mean by "obtained by other means"?'

'It's probable,' I said, 'that we shall pass through regions where the natives are not willing to sell us the things we want to buy.'

'Lieutenant Laronne has taken the words out of my mouth,' said our leader.

'Then I think I understand what you mean,' said Stre. 'In the matter of provisioning, our moral standards may have to be adapted to the demands of a critical situation. We are to use the methods of normal trading wherever possible, but if we encounter people who are unwilling or unresponsive in the matter of commerce, we shall act accordingly.'

'I think you've grasped my meaning correctly,' said Sir John. 'Let's return now to my company of two hundred and fifty bearers or porters. Each man needs a quantity of solid food per day, say rather more than two pounds or about one kilogramme. For a period of four days, two hundred and fifty pagazis will therefore require one thousand kilogrammes of food in all. Between thirty and thirty-five men will be needed to carry these provisions. But the men carrying the food must also be provided with four days' rations, and that will necessitate our having another five bearers.'

'Before we left Bari,' said Stre, 'you emphasized the mathematical aspect of the problem. I found it most interesting. Porters require bearers and bearers in their turn require other bearers. Then too there must be a leader and a staff, and these two require bearers who require bearers. The total number of those engaged on the expedition becomes in fact the sum total of a number of mathematical series. Geometrical series, I believe, for they surely can't be arithmetical. One so easily forgets a terminology one has not used since one's schooldays. Isn't it also possible to talk of a convergent series?'

Sir John had turned towards our doctor. He was listening politely and regarding him benevolently. One might easily have imagined that the lips hidden by his ample moustache were smiling.

'Your manner of reasoning is also very interesting, Dr Stre,' he said. 'This applies particularly to the conclusions you jump to. You have at times, sir, a tendency to jump rather too far. I hope you will excuse my commenting upon it?'

'Why, of course, sir,' answered Stre.

'My comment was directed solely to your manner of arguing or conversing,' said Sir John, 'not to your handling of practical problems. If, for instance, I were to be suffering from an abscess on a toe—a thing that has happened to me—I should confidently place the problem in your hands. I know that, if need be, you would remove the affected toe. On the other hand I should not suffer a moment's uneasiness for fear that, from excessive zeal, you would amputate my whole foot.'

'I'm flattered, sir,' said Dr Stre.

Sir John spoke again:

'We've touched upon two important problems, the question of provisioning and the fact that we shall have with us two companies of askaris.

'Our objective is the relief of the Pasha, nothing else. We shall be passing through what is virtually unexplored territory.'

'We're aware of that,' said Smitt.

'The people who inhabit this territory will, almost without exception, treat us as enemies.'

'What makes you think that, sir?' asked Smitt.

'I'm speaking from experience,' answered Sir John. 'To most primitive peoples the words enemy and stranger are synonymous.'

'But we intend them no harm.'

'We have no intentions about them at all. We simply want to pass through their territory as rapidly as circumstances will permit. We may possibly want to buy provisions from them and I am prepared to pay generously in brass, cloth of the most varying description, pearls, cowries, necklaces of glass beads, or any other acceptable currency.

'The very nature of our task,' he continued, 'means that we really do want to get through their territory as quickly as we can, and yet they will seek to hinder us, and will treat us as enemies.'

'I don't doubt that you're right, sir,' said Smitt. 'But why must things be like that?'

He was answered by Stre:

'Now you're touching upon a really vital problem, Lieutenant Smitt,' he said.

'Perhaps you have a solution to hand, Dr Stre,' said our leader. 'A theoretical solution at least.'

Our doctor shook his head.

'Unfortunately not, Sir John. Perhaps I shall disappoint you if into the bargain I confess that, though I have taken note of the importance of the problem, I am unable to mobilize sufficient interest in it to devote more than fleeting attention to it.'

V

During the few days we spent in Fort John I became convinced that an expedition really is a matter of figures; of the weight of loads, of the number of bearers and soldiers, of men's requirements in the matter of food, of the weight of packages of ammunition, and so forth.

While the loads were being prepared both Sir John and Kingiri were anxious that the weight of each should correspond to two frasilahs at the outside, that is, to about thirty kilograms. This standard weight is not a matter of guesswork. Many years of experience have shown that two frasilahs are a suitable average load for bearers marching in a column.

Of course Dr Stre had some critical comments to make.

'It's easy enough to achieve an average load,' he said, 'but where is your average bearer? People are not cast in the same mould. Barite pagazis are no exception. They are all of them different in build and strength. Twenty-five kilogrammes may seem heavier to one than thirty kilogrammes will to another.'

We could not take his views into account. They were right in principle but impossible to apply in practice.

Our guiding rule, a load of two frasilahs, was applied with consistent exactitude for bearers, but not for soldiers. These men were to carry their weapons and their personal belongings, nothing more. However, the directive issued by Sir John meant that each of our askaris, when he marched out of Fort John, was equipped with a quantity of ammunition which weighed between twenty-nine and thirty kilogrammes. The rifle weighed nine and a half pounds, or approximately four kilogrammes. The weight of their personal belongings was more difficult to estimate. It hovered between two and a half kilogrammes and rather more than ten pounds. Here the thickness of their sleeping-mats was the decisive factor.

When I mentioned this matter to Sir John his only reply was: 'Soldiers are better bearers than bearers. That is one of the reasons why they are soldiers and no longer bearers.'

Our barter-goods alone required a very large number of bearers. The bulk of these goods consisted of bales of cloth, and of brass; the lesser part of cowries, pearls, necklaces of glass beads, and similar articles.

Twenty yards of cloth is worth on the most favourable terms about ten dollars. The texture and colour of the material is also of importance and the estimation of its value varies widely from place to place.

The brass we had with us consisted partly of short rods, about as thick as a forefinger, and partly of brass wire in coils. Sir John's previous experience dictated that the dimensions of the wire should never exceed gauges five or six.

While we were preparing the loads careful notes were made by Sir John's scribe, his moonshee. This latter was a man no longer in his first youth, probably Indian by origin. His appearance was pleasing, and he would have made an entirely agreeable impression if his behaviour to our leader and to us officers had not been marred by an attitude of confidentiality and pretended equality, into which he had probably been beguiled by the nature of his work. He was, of course, always in our company, particularly Sir John's. He wrote rapidly and his handwriting was very legible. He was a good linguist, but also tiresomely garrulous.

VI

Shortly before our departure from the station Sir John informed the Barites that the women and children who had accompanied us from Bari would now have to be left behind.

Sir John's decision caused some unrest. The captains of the Barite companies and some of their subordinates presented themselves at our quarters and obliged us to engage in a long palaver. This was the first that I and my fellow officers had heard of the step that Sir John had taken.

'Even while we were still in Bari,' I said, 'I expressed my doubts about the wisdom of allowing this appendage of women and children.'

'I very well remember our conversation,' answered Sir John.

'Their presence and the complications likely to arise from it have been making me uneasy ever since we left Port Prim.'

'I'm not surprised that you have felt uneasy, Lieutenant Laronne,' said Sir John. 'But you could safely have relied upon me to deal with the cause of your uneasiness.'

'Had you intended, sir,' asked Lieutenant Smitt, 'that these women and children should accompany us all the way to the Pasha?'

'I could not have had any views on the subject in Bari,' answered Sir John. 'An expedition is not merely a question of mathematics. It's also a question of improvisation and adaptation in circumstances which can't be foreseen. It's now, but only now, that I have come to realize that these women and children must be left behind at Fort John.'

'Why did you let them come with us in the first instance?' asked Smitt.

'Your question, Lieutenant Smitt, arises from your ingrained conception of the relationship between men and women. It is so ingrained that you can't imagine any other. In due course you will come to realize that all ingrained ideas and conceptions must, of necessity, be reconsidered.'

'Why must we leave them behind at this particular moment?' asked Dr Stre.

'Because we must make a forced march to Kanyi Pasha.'

'What arrangements have you made for them here in Fort John?'

'I have reached an agreement with the acting head of the station,' replied Sir John. 'A certain sum per person per day will be paid pending our return. Are you inquiring so that the notes in your diary may be as full as possible?'

'Are you certain that we shall return this way?'

'How can I possibly be certain of that?' Sir John replied.

I do not know how many women and children we left behind in Fort John. Not even Sir John's pedantic scribe, the Indian, if he was one, could provide us with precise information on this point.

VII

When Lieutenant Hansen arrived at Fort John with the last boat he was suffering from a mild attack of fever. Five pagazis had deserted during the trip up river. In order to do so they had taken a canoe that we had left behind at the deserted village where we had spent our last night. Before they made off they stole a rifle, a small quantity of ammunition and quite a lot in the way of provisions, likewise the clock and compass from the river-boat and several drums of paraffin.

There had also been trouble between the Barites and Hansen's little escort of Gallas, which he had been unable to prevent because of his illness. One of the Barites had fallen overboard and disappeared. Nobody was sure whether he had been drowned or whether he had fallen because he was dead already.

The boat's mechanic or fireman had tried to separate the combatants, an ambition which had been rewarded by a rather deep wound in the back of his neck.

Dr Stre gave Hansen one gramme of quinine dissolved in four grammes of hydrobromic acid.

Sir John asked him if, contrary to the orders he had received, he had drunk water that had not been boiled. He denied this and Dr Stre remarked:

'I'm entirely of the opinion that water should be boiled. But why, sir? Is it to kill off Koch's bacilli? Or is it to kill miasma? Does miasma die if it is boiled?'

By the time I arrived at Fort John Sir John had already engaged a further seventy bearers from among the natives living on the station or in its immediate surroundings. The Ajantis—or Ajantes—he had selected were young and strong and comparatively light-skinned.

In consultation with the young Italian engineer—the acting head and superintendent at Fort John—a further six Ajantis had been engaged as guides. According to the roll of our men drawn up by our scribe, their headman was called Uli. Perhaps his name might equally correctly have been spelt Oli.

These six guides were each given a Snider, two cases of cartridges, and a panga.

The day before we set off on our march Sir John summoned everyone to a muster and when the roll was called we discovered that twenty Barites and three Gallas were missing.

Sir John appeared quite unperturbed by this falling away of our men. Since he had already engaged seventy Ajantis it is probable that he had foreseen that our numbers would diminish.

Jaffar Topan

In Fort John the wind would increase in violence a couple of hours after sunset and bring with it thunder and heavy rain. Just before midnight it would drop as suddenly as if a door had been shut. The sky would clear and an almost full moon become visible. In the early morning the place was enveloped in dense mist, which was later dispersed by the sun. It would remain windless until after midday. Then that same wind would return and, two hours after sunset, increase in violence bringing in its train thunder and heavy rain.

The days and nights were always the same. Gale, rain, and thunder each evening. In the morning white mist, followed by hot sunshine and calm until the wind returned.

My tent was watertight and we had pitched it in the right place.

The Barites and the Gallas lit large fires at night, and these were their only protection against the weather.

'I should like to stay here,' said Said.

'We must move on,' I answered.

'There are goats and sheep and even cattle here and the pasture is good. Rain falls at night. The days are dry and warm and things are so wisely ordered that the wind begins to blow before the heat has grown too hard to bear.'

'We must cleanse our tent of spiders and snakes before we go to bed,' I said.

'We should be living in a house built of sun-dried mud.'

'All these insects, these clouds of insects!'

'Only for a few hours,' said Said. 'Then the wind will return. They do not trouble us at night if we put out our lamp while we sleep. And this great lake. It is like a small sea; only the salt is lacking.'

'You are very young,' I said.

The shores of the lake were shallow and the waves gathered, rose, and broke sluggishly. In the water was a mat of weed with slimy stalks and tattered leaves, black or very dark green.

Kingiri, the six-fingered captain, was sitting in our tent. He was wet with rain and he held the opening of the tent together with his right hand.

'I have always been a traveller,' he said, 'but I have never been here before. Even if you travel all your life you can still find places you have never visited. I have many times revisited places that I had once left behind me. I have not known where I was. To return is to come again for the first time, no matter how often you return.'

'I should like to stay here, effem,' said Said. 'If you stay you do not need to return.'

'The days are warm and it rains at night,' said Kingiri. 'That is what it is like now. But in a month, or in two or three months, what then? Here too there must be seasons.'

Sir John summoned all seven of the Barite captains to a meeting.

'We shall be obliged to let all the women and children stay here, in Fort John,' he told them.

I explained the meaning of his words.

'Stay here? Leave them here?' Sjimba repeated.

'Leave them here,' I said.

'Why?' he asked.

'They can't come with us and therefore they must stay here,' answered Sir John.

'They have been able to come with us as far as this,' said Sjimba.

Sjimba was the only one of the Barite captains who could read and write, if you except Halmadi, who called himself a Syrt, this people of whom no one has ever heard.

'We must leave them here,' I said.

The captains of the seven companies gathered in a tight knot. The sun had set. It was already dark, but the thunder was still distant and it had not yet begun to rain.

Salaam, the captain of No. 1 Company, spoke:

'You gave us permission to bring them with us.'

Salaam spoke good English and his name was a salutation. His voice was shrill and his hips were rounded like those of a eunuch.

'We all realize that you are not speaking on your own behalf,' I said, 'and that will count in your favour, Salaam, if you are ever in need of something in your favour. But,' I added, 'do not save it up. I am not sure who have the shorter memories, the Europeans or your Barite brothers.'

Sir John spoke:

'I never gave any authorization or permission.'

'You allowed them to come with us, effendim.'

'That was a concession, it was not a promise.'

I explained his meaning:

'Sir John promised you nothing.'

The seven Barites took counsel together for a long time and Sir John waited until they had reached agreement.

Halmadi, the captain of the soldiers, then spoke:

'We have come to the conclusion that you never gave us your promise. But we have also come to the conclusion that you have done us an injury.'

'How great an injury?' asked Sir John.

'One hundred dhotis of cloth to be divided among the injured parties, effendim.'

Sir John announced that he was willing to accept this offer. The Barites took counsel together again and ended by doubling their claim for compensation.

'Two hundred dhotis,' said Halmadi, 'half red and half blue.'

Sir John replied:

'One hundred, no more. That, in itself, is a concession.'

'There are many women and many children. Some of the women are pregnant too.'

'The rain will soon be here,' answered our leader. 'I want to go indoors.'

The Barites took counsel together yet again, and when they had done, they announced that they were willing to accept his suggestion of one hundred dhotis of cloth by way of compensation.

'It was not my suggestion,' he said. 'It was your demand.'

'Not so, effendim. We think that two hundred dhotis would be fair compensation,' answered Halmadi.

The Ajantis were farmers, but at certain times of the year they went hunting and they were also traders in a small way. They journeyed mostly towards the north or the south and exchanged other goods for ivory, which they then sold in Fort John.

The front teeth of many had been filed down, and they seldom wore anything more than a loin-cloth.

I could talk to them in the language spoken by most of the Sultan's servants. The Ajantis used this language when they were on their trading journeys in search of ivory.

Five Barites had made up their minds to desert on our last night in Fort John. They had tried to persuade Said to go with them.

'They don't want to stop here,' he said. 'They are going back down the river.'

They had stolen a canoe and were now sitting hunched up in the rain, waiting for the skies to clear and let the moon shine forth.

'We could have done with a sixth man to paddle,' said one of them. 'Three men paddling on either side would have been better.'

'What are you going to do?' I asked.

'We're going back.'

'Will you find your way back to Bari?'

'If Allah wills it,' answered one of them. 'Our cargo is valuable. The canoe lies deep in the water. Maybe it is just as well that we are only five.'

'We are on our way to Kanyi Pasha,' I said.

'Who is this Pasha? We have never seen him. We do not even know if he exists. He has never seen us. We know that we exist, but he knows nothing about us. We are turning back while there is still time. What makes you want to go on?'

We were speaking into darkness, for we were in a dense thicket close to the shore. The flashes of lightning gave us no light. We could only catch glimpses of them behind or within their clouds. The wind was driving the rain with such force against the leaves that the drumming of it made the claps of thunder sound distant and muffled.

'What makes you want to go on?' my questioner shouted in my ear.

'Why break off a journey once begun?' I said. 'We know what is behind us. What lies before us is new.'

'Who are you?' asked this Barite from somewhere in the darkness, who had seen no more of me than my voice.

'Do you know who Jaffar Topan is?' I asked. 'I am not going on this journey on my own behalf, but because a Bey is far too fat and far too old.

'I can believe that I might stop somewhere,' I said. 'I am not quite sure about myself. I can believe that I might perhaps stop at some pleasant place, especially if someone forced me to do so. But why break off a journey by turning back? Turning back is a poor way of continuing a journey.'

'Effem,' said the Barite—if indeed it was the same man talking all the time, for it is difficult to distinguish between voices in the dark—'to turn back is also a way of experiencing what is new.'

'Perhaps you are right,' I answered. 'I am cold. Most things that happen to me seem one thing when I am cold and another when I am not cold. The rain is warm, the wind is warm, but it makes no difference. These two warm things chill when they happen together. Just now an animal crawled over my hand. I did not move. It might have been a short but rather thick snake, but I think I felt four feet and blunt claws. I should like to know with what things you have loaded your canoe.'

When the wind had abated, and the rain eased off, and the moon was beginning to shine, the five Barites left their hiding-place. They had to wade out far from the shore with their canoe. The waves were huge and aslant, and they found it hard work ploughing through the floating mat of weed, with its tough stalks and large or many small leaves.

'John Effendi has made me responsible for seeing that no one, neither bearer nor soldier, Barite nor Galla, is left behind,' I said to Said, the boy from Amman.

'You have told me so before,' he said.

'I have a list of everybody, name after name, line after line. These five men who are trying to turn back, they are not being left behind, are they?'

Our clothes were wet. We dried them as far as was needful by one of the fires and then went to my tent. Said rolled himself in his mat and fell asleep instantly.

Before sunrise I woke to hear him coughing. When his

coughing did not stop I lit my lamp. He was lying on his back. He was sleeping deeply but restlessly. He had thrown off his mat, and his breast, shoulders and face were shining with sweat, as I remembered seeing Sayyid Bey and the *Avanti*'s Dutch captain shining with sweat.

I turned him on to his side and spread his mat over him.

Sir John's bugler sounded the call for the men to fall in. Their formation had already been rehearsed. They formed up in a square of which one side was missing. This required a good deal of discipline. The companies were marshalled from left to right in numerical order, except that No. 8 Company, that of the Galla soldiers, was placed furthest to the left, and No. 3 Company, that of the Barite soldiers, was furthest to the right. The little group of attendants, water-carriers, tent-pitchers and gun-bearers was squeezed in between the Gallas and Salaam's No. 1 Company.

There is something fascinating about anything that is well ordered.

Even while we were still in Port Prim I had asked Sir John if we ought not to change the numbering of the companies to make it correspond more exactly to this formation of a three-sided square. But the roll of our men had already been drawn up and he rejected my suggestion.

It was early morning and not yet full daylight. The grass and the bushes were still limp with moisture and the mist was hiding everything that was not near at hand.

The bugler had sounded two calls, the first to rouse the men from their sleep, and the second to summon them to fall in. The bugler had been answered by the cocks of Fort John. A herd of goats had collected round him, the sheep had scattered before the all-too-early morning commotion, the sharp-horned cattle had remained unmoved.

Each company had its own bugler and flag-bearer. The

flags of the pagazis were red, white, and blue, those of the two companies of soldiers green.

Lieutenant Laronne, the vakeel, and the six Ajanti guides marched off first. After them came the Galla soldiers with their green flag, and after them the bearers and porters in order of formation, each company headed by its captain and its flag. Halmadi's Barite soldiers brought up the rear.

Seated on a camp-stool, Sir John waited until all the men had marched past him, and out of Fort John in an easterly direction.

'Are you counting them, sir?' I asked.

Beside him was Dr Stre, also waiting.

As it followed the narrowing path the column itself narrowed. The men fell in behind each other and finally they were all marching in one immensely long line.

Sir John and Stre were the last to leave the station. We walked rapidly. We had no heavy burdens to carry, and after a few hours we had caught up with Laronne and the six guides. We were followed by Said, carrying Sir John's stool and rifle, and two of Stre's attendants. One of them was carrying his rifle, and the other balanced on his head the bag which his master always insisted on having with him.

The country in the neighbourhood of the lake was a slightly undulating plain, overgrown with tall grass and dotted with single trees or clumps of trees. The Ajanti villages lay close to each other. As the lake narrowed so too did the plain. The forest to the south of us came nearer. By the time the lake had shrunk to a river again it would reach right down to the banks.

The undulating plain was crossed by ridges or elongated hills. From the highest of these we could see the lake and, after some days, the forest too, a dark green band that seemed to have grown wider each time we saw it, for the simple reason that we were gradually drawing nearer to it.

When we reached the crest of a hill the column looked like a snake winding its way behind us.

'Just like a snake,' I said to John Effendi, 'if it were not far too long. You cannot see the end of it. I have turned to look a hundred times, sir, but the last companies have always been half hidden behind rising ground or hills or dense thickets. At times almost all the men, except those nearest to us, have been quite hidden in the grass.'

We camped at night in Ajanti villages that had been warned of our coming.

Our march began at sunrise and the halt was called one hour before sunset. We rested for a couple of hours at mid-day. On our first day we only marched nine kilometres. On the second day we did five kilometres in the morning and almost seven in the afternoon. By our third day our marching distance had increased to twenty kilometres.

We were following a path, which we trampled harder and wider. The going was easy. We were able to wade most of the water-courses and if they were too deep there were suspension bridges.

The sun was hot but our rest came during the hottest hours. Every afternoon we encountered one or two violent thunderstorms, accompanied by heavy rain. The wind, however, was light and the regular nightly thunderstorms of Fort John had ceased. Even when it rained the path remained hard.

The flag-bearers complained of the weight of their sodden burdens, and said that the flagpoles were chafing their shoulders.

'The going is easy,' I wrote to Sayyid Bey. 'If travelling is a form of piety, as you say it is, then this is not a strenuous sort of piety, especially for those who are not obliged to carry anything.

'The nights are warm,' I wrote. 'The moon is on the wane, and if the traveller's night is reckoned as part of his journey, then it is the nights that earn him the greater part of his piety. The air is full of insects, all of them larger, more vicious, and more poisonous than those we have in Bari.

'Halmadi, the melancholy captain of the askaris, quotes the words of the Prophet: "Allah has bestowed garments upon the children of Adam so that they may hide their nakedness, but the garment of godliness is an even better thing."

'Most of Adam's Barite children,' I wrote, 'have received far too few garments from Allah and their godliness is clearly all too insignificant to preserve their nakedness from the attacks of the mosquitoes.

'Halmadi has made many pilgrimages to Mecca. He wraps himself in his woollen mantle as if he were a sufi. The mantle is threadbare, but dirt and grease and age have made it as hard as a tunic of mail. Once he has rolled himself in his mat there is but little nakedness left to be covered by the garment of his godliness.

'Upon me, the unbeliever,' I wrote, 'Allah has bestowed a tent.'

Each day we received our ration of a pound of rice and an equal weight of cassava bread.

We were well received in the Ajanti villages.

On the fifth day Lieutenant Smitt went ahead with some of the Galla soldiers and three Ajantis. He managed to shoot two hippopotamuses, so there was enough meat for everyone. We ate for the whole of the sixth day, which was a day of rest, and by evening nothing was left but the white bones.

The further we got from Fort John the more scattered grew the villages. The one in which we spent our third night was surrounded by a simple palisade of dry, thorny brushwood. As we went on and got even further from Fort John, the palisades surrounding the villages became taller and thicker.

'Have you noticed, effendim,' I asked Sir John, 'that the villages grow smaller and the distance between them increases, but that village by village the palisades that surround them grow taller and thicker?'

'We can sleep all the more confidently,' he answered.

As the villages grew smaller, we were more crowded together at night and could light fewer fires. Sometimes fierce fighting broke out between the Barites and the Gallas.

Laronne was the lightest sleeper of the lieutenants and he would quickly intervene with his long rattan switch. On one occasion a fire-brand was thrown at him. He was more dazzled than burnt, but he hurled himself at the man nearest to him, a Galla, as it happened, and they both fell to the ground.

The end of the switch in Laronne's hand was pointed and in their fall this sharp end penetrated the other man's calf.

The soldier to whom this happened was the man they call Five Pounds, one of Dajatsj's subordinates, and the man who had been with Laronne and me when we were journeying up the river.

The wound was not very deep. He washed it with water until it stopped bleeding.

Laronne

I

We had taken with us from Bari seven horses and a number of donkeys and mules. Some of the latter animals were unable to stand the journey by sea. Others ate themselves to death when they were put out to graze in Port Prim. Those that remained died on our way up river, with the exception of three or four which disappeared shortly after we arrived at Fort John.

While we were travelling up the river our seven horses were attacked by a disease the symptoms of which were an inflammation of the mouth and of the sensitive portions of their anatomy between their hind legs.

These horses caused a great stir in Fort John, and I believe I am right in supposing that the Ajantis had never before seen one.

We had intended to use them partly as pack-horses but primarily as saddle-horses. During the days we spent at the station they began to show signs of recovery, but when we were ready to set out we realized that it would be impossible to use them in either capacity. They had therefore to be led by the Galla soldiers marching in the van of the expedition. Five of them had to carry their saddles as we were very short of bearers.

For two days the horses still appeared to be on the mend, but on the third day they grew restless and unmanageable and only proceeded willingly if they could smell water. On the fourth day they showed clear signs of increasing weakness. Their restlessness subsided, and when our pace slackened on an incline they would stand still and refuse to move at all.

On the afternoon of the fifth day we arrived early at the Ajanti village where we were to spend the night. At Sir John's request Dr Stre examined the horses and found that their lymphatic glands were very swollen and their mouths so much inflamed that they could no longer graze. Practically all the horses had identical symptoms.

'I'm a doctor, not a vet,' said Stre. 'I can only give you my advice, I can't prescribe. I don't know much about horses. I'm neither a farrier nor a groom. I can't even remember what the normal temperature of a horse should be.'

The village to which we had come was near the lake. Sir John gave orders that a deep grave should be dug in a line with the shore. The sand was very fine and the surface dry and shifting, but further down it was damp and very hard.

There were too many Barites digging. They kept bumping into each other and getting in each other's way. But Sir John remained in the vicinity all the time and I therefore hesitated to intervene and reduce the labour-force he seemed to consider necessary.

One of the diggers received an unintentional blow on the head from the spade of one of his mates. Quite a lot of blood ran down his back, but the actual wound was hidden by hair and sand. He could not see over his shoulders and appeared quite insensitive to pain. He behaved exactly as if he had been stung by an ant, shook his head and shoulders, moved a step to one side and went on digging.

The seven horses were led up to the grave one by one.

They were then shot between the eyes and fell, by their own weight, into the space allotted to them.

On this particular day Lieutenant Smitt had gone off on a short hunting expedition. He had come upon a herd of hippopotamuses and managed to shoot two, a feat of which he was all the more proud, because both Sir John and the Ajantis declared that only a small number of these animals were to be found in the lake.

Smitt was noticeably upset when he heard that the horses had been shot.

'The responsibility is yours,' he said to Stre.

'I made a diagnosis in general terms,' answered our doctor. 'I didn't prescribe anything.'

'What disease were they suffering from?' asked Smitt.

'I'm a doctor, not a vet.'

Sir John intervened:

'You're a biologist, aren't you, Lieutenant Smitt?'

'Really a zoologist, sir. The difference is considerable and grows greater every year.'

'Have you any views about the state the horses were in?'

'I believe in principle, sir, that a horse should never be put to death until one is absolutely certain that it's necessary.'

At this point Sir John put an end to any further discussion.

'You hold one view, Lieutenant Smitt, and you another, Dr Stre, but in the last resort it is I who decide what is to be done.'

II

A number of bearers were missing when we left Fort John and we had no time to look for them. During the following days a further number absconded. These defections did not cause any acute difficulties. Two of the deserters had taken their loads with them, but we were able to transfer the loads left behind to Ajantis or to Barites who had been carrying provisions, but whom our daily consumption of rice and cassava had left without loads.

'We've lost eight bearers,' I said to Sir John.

'That's not remarkably many,' he answered. 'Very soon we shall lose another eight men and after that eight more and then another eight on top of that. What number have I reached now? Sixteen plus eight, in addition to those who've already disappeared.'

'We must put a stop to it,' I said.

'I'm more sorry to have lost the twelve Snider rifles and the ammunition they've taken with them. The men who desert at the start are the ones who would have given us trouble later on. You might even call this a process of natural selection. Have you read *The Origin of Species*, Lieutenant Laronne?'

'I'm quite certain,' said Dr Stre, 'that that is not a book which is included in the reading-matter studied at a Military Academy.'

Ignoring both Sir John's question and Stre's remark I said:

'Even if we regard these desertions as a link in the process of natural selection, sir, I don't imagine that we can regard them as permissible, can we?'

'Of course we can't,' he answered, 'and it's important that we should be increasingly on the alert.'

III

After leaving Fort John our route led us at first across the savannah-like country that extended along the shore of the large lake. According to reports there was similar country on the opposite side of the lake as well.

Smitt asserted that this was not a true savannah. We were,

in fact, far from the real savannah region, he said. He believed that this plain was the result of special climatic conditions created by the presence of the lake, the most important being that it enabled the wind to blow freely.

Sir John agreed with him.

'This is a sort of pseudo-savannah,' he said. 'The resemblance to genuine savannah country is illusory. This applies not only to the vegetation, but even more to the fauna. This country is almost totally lacking in the true savannah's superabundance of animal life.'

In spite of the fact that we rested for two hours at midday the heat of the sun troubled us a good deal. I myself had succeeded in becoming acclimatized and suffered considerably less than the others. Smitt was still plagued by his much too fair skin and light eyes. He tried to protect himself by wearing a cap with a wide peak and hanging neck-shield, and you might have thought he was an officer of *la légion étrangère*. Hansen and Stre drank large quantities of water and sweated accordingly.

Stre prescribed salt-tablets, to be taken every morning and evening.

Sir John remarked:

'When people first began to establish commercial relations with the peoples of tropical regions the most important article of currency was salt. One of the pioneers of long ago, I can't now remember which, mentioned in a memoir that was subsequently published that the natives valued salt more highly than gold, and that they needed it to cool their blood.'

Each day we encountered two or more thunderstorms, accompanied by torrential rain, but they were quickly over and only served to increase the prevailing heat.

The distance we covered in each march was measured by Sir John by means of a pedometer. Every third or fourth day he checked and supplemented the values thus obtained with a sextant and a chronometer. He also kept a daily record of the altitude of our nightly camping-places by taking readings from two aneroids.

'I'm well aware that my altitude readings are very approximate,' he said, 'and that secondary changes in air pressure affect my figures to an extent which it is difficult to estimate. Nevertheless, it is better to have debatable altitude readings than none at all.'

A daily record of the weather, the wind, and the temperature was also kept. The temperature was measured three times a day, at sunrise, at sunset, and when the sun was at its height. He had two thermometers, one wet and one dry, both calibrated on the Centigrade scale.

'Are all these observations really necessary?' Hansen asked me on one occasion.

'Do they annoy you?' I asked.

'I hope you won't misunderstand me, sir,' he said, averting his gaze. 'I think I've been what is usually known as well brought up. Before we left Bari it would never have occurred to me to criticize anything Sir John chose to do, more especially as he is my superior officer.'

'I think I know what you mean, Lieutenant Hansen.'

'I don't understand,' he said, 'the connection between our task of relieving the Pasha and Sir John's diligence in constantly making notes and observations.'

'Do you feel,' I asked, 'that to keep track of how far we have marched and of where we are is a work of supererogation?'

'To do that is perfectly reasonable, and I must say that I'm impressed by these experts in navigation who can handle a sextant. Can you, Lieutenant Laronne? Perhaps it's quite a simple matter for those who have learnt the art. But all these temperature readings? And our height above sea-level, and whether it rains, and if so at what time of day, and in what quantity approximately? What has all this to do with the object of the expedition?'

'Very likely nothing,' I answered. 'But, on the other hand, these occupations don't obstruct our progress. We are never delayed because Sir John likes to devote some of his time to making certain observations.'

Hansen sat for a long time in my tent without speaking.

'You're right, of course,' he said after a while.

'All the same it annoys you?'

'Rather, it makes me a little uneasy, sir,' answered Hansen.

IV

On the evening when we had arranged to spend the night in an Ajanti village for the last time, I was summoned to Sir John.

He informed me that he had finally decided upon the order in which our expedition was to march, and he handed me written directions which he asked me to study.

Our men were to be divided into three groups. The first was to consist of the Galla soldiers and No. 4 Company, Sjimba's bearers. About half the Ajanti bearers—most of them for the moment without loads—were also to be attached to this group, likewise the Ajanti guides. This group was to be directly under Sir John's command.

The third and last group was to consist of our Barite askaris, captained by Halmadi.

The second and centre group, which was the largest, comprised practically speaking all our bearers, porters and attendants.

The rearguard was to be commanded by Lieutenant Smitt, while the supervision of the main body was assigned to Hansen.

'You, Lieutenant Laronne,' Sir John said, 'are, for all essential purposes, attached to the advance guard, likewise Dr Stre. Have you any objections to put forward?'

'No, sir,' I answered.

'In your capacity of my second-in-command I want to give you the opportunity of hearing my decisions before I make them known to the others,' he said.

Thereupon, with Said's help, he had Hansen, Smitt and Dr Stre called, and gave each one a copy of the directions he had drawn up.

'I notice with satisfaction,' said our doctor, 'that you intend to continue to maintain the greatest possible distance between the Galla and the Barite soldiers. The former find it difficult to get on well with the Barites, and the lack of harmony is particularly noticeable in their relations with the Barite soldiers. I have had a quite unnecessary amount of trouble over wounds and other injuries on this account.'

Sir John handed each one of us a by-no-means-brief memorandum in which he had concisely phrased his views on how we ought to behave in future, what precautions we ought to take, what independent actions by us would be tolerated, or not tolerated, and what demands he considered he had the right to make upon us.

The four copies of the memorandum had been written out by his Indian servant. I had learnt to recognize his clear, legible handwriting. He had used black ink, not blue.

It is very uncertain if he really was an Indian, though we constantly referred to him as one. His attire reminded one most of the clothing worn by upper-class Arabs in certain parts of the Mediterranean area, but his appearance and his behaviour did not indicate a Semitic or Hamitic origin. It may be that we had come to regard him as an Indian partly because our leader sometimes called him moonshee and partly because he was clearly neither a Christian nor a Muslim.

Jaffar Topan

On our last night but one in an Ajanti village I was woken before sunrise by Halmadi, the woollen-mantled captain of the Barite askaris. By opening the flap of the tent he let insects and cool air stream in over me and Said. When you have slept for a whole night in a well-sealed tent even oppressively warm morning air feels like a cooling bath.

'Salaam,' I said. 'What is it you want? Do not wake the boy Said, if he has not yet woken up.'

I stepped over the sleeper and let the flap of the tent fall to behind me.

Halmadi led the way, and I followed him in the rapidly dispersing gloom that heralds the sunrise. You could not with certainty have distinguished a thread of black wool from a thread of white.

He led me to the only exit there was in the wall of thorn-bushes that surrounded the village. This was kept closed at night by scattering quantities of thorny twigs and poisonous plants over the hard and fairly wide path that led through it.

Halmadi stopped, and indicated with an outstretched foot the prostrate figure of a Barite soldier pierced through by a Galla spear. It had been driven into his left shoulder near his neck and his collar-bone with such force that the point had emerged between his ribs and his right hip.

'He is dead,' I said. 'What is it you want?'

Four or five askaris were squatting close to the skewered body.

I went to Sir John's tent and waited while he dressed, and as I waited the morning gloom was driven away by the sun.

'A Barite soldier is lying dead,' I said, and led him to the village gateway.

He asked what had happened and why this had been done, but the Barites gave him no answer.

Halmadi said:

'Allah has created man of clay like an earthen vessel. He is the Lord of the East as He is the Lord of the West. He has also created the Jinn, but of fireless smoke, not clay. This is written in the sura called The Merciful.'

'Something must have happened,' repeated Sir John.

In response to an order from Halmadi one of the Barites drew the Galla spear out of the dead man's body. This was not done without difficulty. He gave it to Halmadi, who in his turn threw it down at Sir John's feet.

'The sinners will be recognized by their marks,' said the askaris' captain, 'and they will be seized by the forelock and by the feet.'

A blast on the bugle summoned the Galla soldiers to a muster by the body of the prostrate Barite.

'What do you know about this?' asked John Effendi.

'Nothing,' answered Dajatsj.

Our leader pointed with his stick to the Galla spear lying before him on the grass.

'Have you seen a spear like this before?'

'Many times, sir.'

'But you know nothing?'

Dajatsj went up to the dead man, examined him and turned his body half over.

'He must have been sitting when he was killed,' he

said. 'That is all I know. The spear was driven in from above.'

Sir John and Laronne walked along the lines of the assembled Gallas. Each man had his three spears, some carried four.

'And the spear?' asked the Galla captain.

'What do you mean?'

'Are we to leave it where it is?'

'Take it,' answered Sir John, 'you who nevertheless know nothing.'

Dajatsj snatched up the spear, now quite dry. He weighed it in his hand and then gave it to one of his subordinates.

The dead soldier was buried. The Barites handled their spades clumsily. They lifted them high in the air and brought them down rather as if they had been some sort of mattock. They could not use their feet, for they were unshod, and even if the soles of their feet were hard and thick from always walking barefoot, they were not hard or insensitive enough to press an iron spade into the earth.

Because of this incident our departure was delayed and we were only able to cover a short stretch before our midday rest.

The path grew softer. The isolated trees were now nearer each other, the little groves were denser and the prickly thickets extended over a wider area. We could no longer see the lake.

It was a very hot day. At our midday rest Sir John had a canvas awning stretched over the spot where they had put his easy chair and the table at which he, Laronne, and Stre ate. Hansen and Smitt were further in the rear of the column, and they were not usually united with those at its head until we reached our night-quarters.

During the meal a Barite approached Sir John's hillock. He sat down to wait until they had finished their meal, though not too far off to prevent him from enjoying the shade cast by the awning.

He was wearing a green fez and an embroidered green tunic fastened at the front. His arms were covered down to his wrists and only the shanks of his legs were bare. His skin was light in colour and he sat motionless until Sir John had finished his meal and Said had carried away the table. Then he rose and drew closer to them.

'Salaam, alekum,' he said and bowed.

'What do you want?' asked Sir John. 'What is your name? I have not seen you before.'

'Kitete.'

'Is that your name?'

'Yes, effendim,' answered the Barite. 'He who was killed last night was called Bandangi, but I called him Ali.'

'That is quite true, sir,' I said. 'I have struck his name from the roll—Bandangi, called Ali.'

'What is it you want?' asked our leader.

'I bought him less than four months ago,' answered Kitete. 'He was young and strong and I paid accordingly. I myself am a bearer, but he was young and strong enough to be a soldier.'

Kitete spoke slowly and clearly. It was impossible to misunderstand him. Nevertheless I repeated what he had said.

'Sir, Kitete says he bought this Ali, or Bandangi, who is now dead, and that he paid a considerable sum for him because of his youth and strength.' To the Barite I said:

'John Effendi does not understand why you have come to him. He asks what it is you want to say.'

'Ali would have received a yearly wage of eight pounds,' replied Kitete. 'I shall now lose that money. I paid six pounds for him and I shall lose that too. What has happened was no fault of mine.'

Sir John had seated himself in his easy chair. He was drinking coffee and smoking his pipe and was regarding the Barite with great serenity.

'You consider that you have sustained a loss, Kitete,' he said. 'Your name is Kitete, I presume, and not Ali?'

'Nor is his name Bandangi,' I said.

'You consider that you have sustained a loss,' said Sir John. 'I gather that you want compensation for this loss?'

'Yes, effendim,' replied Kitete, the well-clothed Barite.

Sir John smoked for a long time in silence. Kitete waited hopefully. He stood with his legs wide apart, relaxed, leaning against one of the posts over which the canvas was stretched.

'You will not get any compensation,' said our leader at last. 'The position is this: no man can own another human being, not even if he has bought him for six pounds. I suspect that you paid four pounds for him at the outside, but that is beside the point. Ali's death was a misfortune for Ali, not for you. You may go, Kitete. We shall soon be resuming our march. You are not as young and strong as Ali was. It is very hot and you need your midday rest. No man can own another man.'

Kitete remained where he was, still leaning against the post. His face was narrow and his eyes were small, and in all probability he had been listening attentively.

Laronne got up.

'You can go now,' he said. 'You can go, Kitete!'

The Barite did not move.

Sir John's vakeel gave him a smart blow with his rattan switch.

'Once more, effendim,' said Kitete.

Laronne struck him another blow, harder than the first, which tore a rent in one sleeve of the Barite's shirt.

'I will go,' said Kitete, and departed without haste.

'That was unwise of you, Lieutenant Laronne,' said Sir John.

'You told him to go and he didn't.'

'He wouldn't have stayed much longer.'

'I can't define it exactly,' said our leader. 'But my experience tells me that you acted unwisely.'

Late on the evening of our last night in an Ajanti village I was called to Sir John's tent. A paraffin lamp was suspended from a tripod made of three long bamboo poles. The six guides were all there within the circle of light. Five were crouching, the sixth standing upright. The man standing was Uli, their headman. He was tall, and like most Ajantis he had a lithe body, filed teeth, and pierced ears. On his head, as a token of his rank, he wore a helmet made of plaited copper strips.

Uli and the other bearers had little with which to hide their nakedness beside their cartridge-belts and the rolled-up mats they carried over one shoulder.

'What do they want?' asked Sir John.

'Yesterday the Barite Kitete came to you on a matter of business,' I said. 'Now the Ajanti guides have gathered here. Most likely they too have some business to discuss. Twenty-four hours is an insignificant interval of time, sir.

To Uli I said: 'What do you want?'

'This is the last Ajanti village,' answered Uli. 'Our country ends here. I was born here, and my father killed many crocodiles in this river. That was when I was a child. Since then I have never lived here. The huts in this village are not built of sun-dried mud but of the branches of trees and reeds.'

To Sir John I said:

'It was in this very village that Uli slipped forth from between his mother's legs, but it is also here that the country of the Ajantis ends. He has guided us here, and for this service he and the other Ajantis have received a modest reward.'

'How much do you demand in future?' I asked Uli, and he replied:

'The road to this place was in one direction only. This is where I was born. From this village our road goes in two directions.'

'Why in two directions?' I asked.

'We must first go east,' he said, 'and then we must return.'

'Up to now the Ajantis have been in their own country,' I said to Sir John. 'If they now continue towards the east, in course of time they will have to return. Hence their road will be in two directions. From this moment, therefore, they wish to be paid double, effendim.'

Sir John sent Said for his easy chair and he sat in it as he had done when he talked to Kitete, the well-clad Barite.

'We agreed on a wage,' he said, 'a daily wage. Tell him what I say. I have kept my part of the bargain, he must keep his.'

'Our bargain is only valid as far as this,' answered Uli.

'He says that you have misunderstood him,' I said to Sir John. 'Ajanti country ends here and with it your bargain. He does not blame you for misunderstanding him. Tomorrow he will return to Fort John without bearing you a grudge.'

Sir John lit his pipe and smoked for a long time in silence. Uli waited expectantly, astraddle and relaxed, leaning on his Snider.

Finally Sir John spoke:

'Pay them double? Double wages? I can't deny that they will have to march in two directions, but the road back to the stable is appreciably shorter than the road from it.'

'We are prepared to pay you half as much again for the return journey,' I said to Uli. 'Not twice as much, only half as much again.'

The copper-helmeted headman of the Ajanti guides looked questioningly over his shoulder at the five who were seated on the grass behind him. They looked at each other. They were in no hurry, it was only evening, not yet night. One of them said something. His utterance was brief, and you could not hear whether he had spoken three words or seven.

'We are content,' answered Uli.

'They ask you to raise their daily wage by half,' I said to Sir John.

'It shall be done,' he answered.

Laronne, the vakeel, asked:

'I suppose this only applies to the guides? To these five men and the one with the copper cap? Not to the rest of the Ajantis?'

'The other Ajantis are paid by the month,' I said. 'It is only the guides who get a daily wage. Sir, the air is humid and the sky is overcast. It is very warm. It will not be long before the rain is upon us.'

To Uli I said: 'You have got your way.'

The six Ajanti withdrew backwards out of the circle of light cast by the hanging paraffin lamp.

'I do not wish to offer any criticism, Sir John,' said Laronne. 'Such an idea would never enter my head.'

'You think I have been too compliant,' said our leader from his easy chair.

'The expression is yours, not mine.'

'Experience has taught me,' Sir John continued, 'that you can coerce bearers and soldiers, sometimes successfully, sometimes unsuccessfully. But I have also learnt that you can never coerce guides, least of all with a rattan switch. Is Dr Stre here?'

'He has gone to his tent, effendim,' I answered.

*

The path had grown softer and the isolated trees were now nearer together. They were all so near to each other that they no longer stood in clumps. The thickets had become more extensive, they were now able to spread themselves over two ridges and the valley between. They were prickly and seemingly impenetrable and compelled us to make long detours.

We were approaching the forest. There were more and more birds, not only birds that flew, but also those that seemed unwilling to leave the ground, short-winged running creatures, like stunted dogs, that scattered in all directions.

The path we were following branched and became two paths. Uli chose the right-hand one. This path also split into two, and Uli chose the left-hand one.

On the plain we had been tormented by the sun. Now there was an ever-diminishing distance between the shade-giving trees. We were about to enter the forest.

From the rear of the advance guard I could hear a drum beating and Barite songs.

The path wound its tortuous way among the ever-larger and ever-denser thickets. The wind died away and the air was laden with scents one can only call overpowering. The grass grew shorter, but at the same time greener and damper.

We lost our open view. When I turned round I could see Sjimba's flag, but seldom the flag carried at the head of the main body, the one that belonged to Salaam's or Abdul the Ninety-ninth's company.

We marched into a cloud of butterflies. It hung like mist above the path, reaching almost to the tree-tops and perhaps two thousand feet in length. It is possible that it was less dense at its outer edges, but you could not see through it in the centre. I have never before beheld such a mass of living creatures.

The butterflies' fluttering advance was rather slower than our marching-pace. We caught them up, went into their midst, through the cloud and out on the other side. It took us almost half an hour.

The Ajanti guides laid about them with their pangas in order that they might breathe freely. The butterflies smothered our faces, and we had to protect our mouths and noses with our hands. Thousands of them were killed under our arms or between our legs, perhaps hundreds of thousands.

Their wings were yellow, but in spite of their colour they hid the sun and made everything dim and grey. Marching out of this cloud of butterflies was like emerging from a dismal fog of millions of senselessly fluttering wings.

We stopped for our midday rest on a low hill between four trees whose branches had grown together to form a single crown. Close by the hill there flowed a sluggish, shallow stream of oily water. Said made coffee for Sir John, Laronne and Stre. The smoke from his fire drifted between the four trunks and up under their common crown.

The Galla soldiers and Sjimba's pagazis ate a piece of cassava and drank the oily water.

Around us were many tall trees and between them a dense undergrowth of bushes and plants.

One tree was naked and dead. It had lost both leaves and creepers, even the bark had fallen off. Gigantic wasps' nests hung from its branches. Some were at least ten feet long, and on the ground were the remains of one that had been even bigger.

'Not only butterflies,' I said to Said.

'No,' he answered.

The dense undergrowth was smothered with flowers of all colours, and these flowers were turned towards us. 'Wasps and bees eat flowers,' said Said, 'but butterflies are themselves a kind of flower. Or, Jaffar, are they a kind of very small bird?'

Our midday rest was short. We did not need long rests, we were still well fed and well rested.

After they were themselves at a safe distance some of the last of the Gallas shot the two largest wasps' nests to pieces. They had probably stuffed gravel and bits of lead into the muzzles of their rifles to make the shots more effective.

Sjimba's Barites fell into a panic. They surged upon the men ahead and obliged all the forward troops, the whole of the advance guard, to march at the double. Many people were severely stung.

Our route grew more and more winding. Uli turned sometimes to the right, sometimes to the left. He chose without hesitation and never paused.

We reached a region of luxuriant vegetation and waterlogged ground. The Ajanti guides leapt from tussock to tussock. Dajatsj's soldiers did not leap. They marched straight ahead, putting one foot in front of the other. The Gallas' footsteps are heavy, and their feet sank into the spongy ground. They tramped a rut, and the more of them who followed it, the one behind the other, the deeper and blacker it grew.

'We knew that the forest would be here,' I said to Said. 'Every day when we were crossing the Ajantis' plain we could see the large lake to the north of us, and sometimes we marched along its shore. But to the south we could also see the forest, that is, we could see it from the highest of the hills if we turned our eyes in the right direction.'

'A green streak,' he answered.

'That grew and became broader.'

'That drew nearer.'

'We knew that we must enter it.'

'Yes, effem,' answered Said.

In a letter to Sayyid Bey I wrote:

'We knew that the forest was there and that we must enter it. There were foreshadowings of it too. In the Ajanti country the distance between the trees and groves diminished, the thickets grew larger and denser while, at the same time, the grass became shorter and the ground softer. The birds increased in number, but I have not yet seen a vulture or a kite. We have marched through a cloud of butterflies and been pursued by a cloud of wasps.

'Have I not already asked you whether the Prophet ever had the opportunity of seeing a river?' I wrote. 'You have yourself told me that he was a man. A man's life is short, but journeys require a long time. Did Ahmed ibn Abdullah, called Mohammed, ever journey through a forest?

'Notwithstanding the foreshadowings we had of it, marching into the forest was like entering a green wall. On the day before we did so the path we had followed up till then grew increasingly insignificant and less trodden. We changed its appearance by reason of our many footsteps, but that is another matter. Yet, even if the path had narrowed, we still had the open sky above our heads. Even if the path grew ever more winding, we still had open space about us, if you except the two clouds of butterflies and wasps. When we marched into the forest the path became a tunnel. We were marching into a green wall.

'The sun disappeared, though I can remember no clouds. It took time before our eyes grew accustomed to the green gloom. We marched in oppressive heat that might have been a Turkish bath, had it not been all too damp and all too long-lasting.

'The path through the tunnel was narrow,' I wrote, 'sometimes not more than three and a half feet wide. Six Ajanti went in front with hatchets. They did not widen the path for us, only cleared it of the lianas and branches that blocked it.

'Said asked me if a butterfly was a flower or a very small bird. He is only a boy, born in Amman.

'There is one thing that surprises me,' I wrote. 'It is the silence that reigns since we entered the forest. Sjimba's bearers have ceased to sing. They all march in silence, singing no songs in the heart of this tunnel. The only sounds we hear are the blows of the Ajantis' hatchets. The Ajantis' headman is called Uli and he wears a copper helmet.

'I know that what I experience as silence is not true silence. The forest is full of sounds. The monkeys—there are masses of them—both chatter and howl. A single one of the loudest-voiced among them could drown the voice of a lion. The birds—there are masses of them too—are certainly not dumb. Some of them only croak, others have a shriller cry. Some can be heard at a great distance. Some sound like drummers, others remind me of trumpeters. We cannot see them; they are high above our heads, for we are walking in a tunnel. The air of this tunnel is itself a well of sound, it is full of wasps, little bees, big bees, mosquitoes, flies, gadflies, and thousands of other insects, whose names I do not know and do not want to know. The tunnel trembles and drones like the engines of a ship. Not even the ground is silent. Cicadas and crickets creak like the unoiled chain of a very deep well. There are frogs here that do not croak, but keep up a long-drawn-out rattling not unlike the sound of distant rifle-fire. They are far from shy, rather inquisitive. At every tenth step, Sayyid Bey, I have to kick one of these frogs out of my way.

'Thus, as you see, the forest is itself a multiplicity of sound, and yet I experienced the first hours we spent in it as a brief moment of deep silence.

'Is it not true that ears have been given us that we may

apprehend sound?' I wrote to Sayyid. 'But there must be sounds that our ears cannot hear. The path through the forest teems at times with gigantic beetles, black, shiny creatures as long as a forefinger and almost as thick. Treading on such a beetle is like crushing a head, but you hear the crunch of it not with your ears, but with your heels and your legs.

'When we marched into the forest our unaccustomed ears were met by a silence that numbed them, and forced Sjimba's bearers to desist from singing,' I wrote.

'There is silence in the green gloom. There is silence too in the tremendous size of the trees. Their trunks are bigger than minarets, and they are clad with moss and climbing plants. I cannot say how high they are for our path is a tunnel. Their branches are intermingled, and from branch to branch and from tree to tree hangs a close network of lianas and, interwoven with these, a still closer network of plants, whose names I do not know, but whose blooms are so heavy that, merely by falling, one could kill a Barite, and whose leaves are so huge that one alone would suffice to shroud the Barite so killed.

'Many of the trees have ten, twenty or thirty roots,' I wrote. 'They spring from the trunks of the trees so high up that only with an effort can a Galla soldier reach them with his bundle of three spears. You might think that these ten or thirty roots were branches going in the wrong direction, but that they have no leaves. Each one of them splits up into innumerable rootlets before it buries itself in the soil.

'The walls of our path are not made of giant trees,' I wrote. 'They are made of bushes and plants and lianas. Some of these bushes are so dense that you can hardly drive a stick into them. There are also bushes that are so full of long, tough thorns that the bearer who stumbled and fell into one would be mortally wounded.

'Do you understand, Sayyid, why it was that at first the forest seemed to me a multiplicity of silence? Are you smoking your hookah? If you are, then read my letter again tomorrow. If not, then light your pipe before you read it again.'

Laronne

I

Sir John caused the halt to be sounded a good hour before sunset. The Ajantis, the Galla soldiers, and the Barites received orders to make a sufficiently large clearing with the aid of their pangas.

Sjimba had done this kind of thing before and knew what a boma or zariba should look like. Dajatsj, the Galla captain, was more hesitant and unsure of himself, but he and his men were quick to learn.

All the undergrowth and the lianas were removed from an almost circular area of about a hundred and fifty paces in diameter. The site was well chosen, and the ground was as dry as circumstances would allow.

The brushwood from what had recently been thickets was piled up in two semicircular walls facing each other. These were the palisade of our boma. It had two entrances, as the semicircles did not quite meet.

Our boma was not finished when Hansen's men, who formed the main body, arrived, and its bearers were therefore made to lend a hand with the work. Most of them were tired and unwilling, but their contribution was nevertheless valuable, a fact that was clearly due to old Kingiri's authority and determination.

Among other things he pointed out that, though the men who had made the initial clearing had certainly removed the undergrowth inside the boma, their pangas had left a great many stumps which were almost hidden by moss. These were unduly sharp because the blows had been aimed too much in a downward direction, and they therefore constituted a danger to anyone who happened to tread on them.

Smitt's rearguard, consisting of our company of Barite soldiers, was able to march into night-quarters prepared and ready to receive it.

The sun was just going down. Only faint traces of daylight remained and these rapidly faded into the darkness of night.

We pitched our tents in the centre of the boma. These had been made by a sail-maker in Plymouth according to Sir John's instructions. They were reasonably roomy and afforded ample space for our beds, and such personal belongings as we required at night, or which we liked to keep under cover. Sir John had brought two tents for himself, one of which was intended for our common use at mealtimes.

II

Just as we were about to take our places at table on our first evening in the forest a torrential storm of rain, accompanied as usual by thunder and gale-force winds, descended upon us. The tempest itself was not very noticeable because of the height of the trees, and the density of the vegetation, but the rain collected by leaves and lianas poured down upon the earth in jets of tremendous force.

Sir John seemed in unusually high spirits, almost gay. He welcomed us to the meal with exaggerated courtesy, asked how we had fared on our march through the forest, but, before any of us had had time to answer, passed on to praising the quality and watertightness of the material of which the tent was made, which he attributed entirely to the fact that he had insisted on having it impregnated with copper sulphate.

'Tents have one weakness,' he said. 'The mosquito-net at the opening protects us from flying insects, but all the wingless little devils that creep have a highly developed talent for insinuating themselves at the point where the base of the tent touches the ground.'

'Couldn't you solve that problem, sir,' asked Dr Stre, 'by having the piece of canvas that constitutes the floor of the tent sewn to the pieces that form its walls and roof?'

'I have, of course, considered that possibility,' replied our leader. 'The matter is entirely one of weighing up alternatives. Space and comfort against weight. The canvas which forms the floor must necessarily be made of thick, and consequently heavy, material. The tent in which we are now sitting weighs very nearly four frasilahs, of which almost half is accounted for by the flooring. In other words, it is the equivalent of two loads and requires two bearers. Experience has taught me that one should, if possible, avoid items of baggage so heavy that they have to be carried on a pole between two bearers. I can very well imagine a tent sewn together in the way you suggest, Dr Stre, but it would have to be pretty small if its weight were to correspond to a man's load. A small tent implies a reduced standard of comfort. The whole problem, as I said, is one of weighing up alternatives.'

'The light-coloured groundsheet has at any rate one advantage,' said Hansen. 'You can very easily detect the uninvited creepy-crawlies.'

'My young friend,' replied Sir John, 'you are overlooking two important factors. Firstly, the groundsheet will very soon lose its light colour, and secondly, a large part of the insects who will pester us in future are so small that several of them could creep simultaneously through the eye of a needle without causing any congestion. They are minute. They can wriggle without difficulty through the material of the tent. They fall into your spoon just as you are lifting it from your soup-plate and you don't know anything about it until they begin to burrow into the mucous membrane of your stomach. On this particular evening there is no cause for alarm. The rain is, in that respect, a blessing, as it has made the canvas impenetrable. There is another species of living creature, Lieutenant Hansen, which will also brighten your life for you in future without your being aware of its existence before it, and hundreds of its fellows, have established themselves under your toe-nails. I do not know whether they are beetles, ants, fleas, grubs or larvae. They are visible under a magnifying glass of medium strength, but they have caused me so much suffering that I have not been able to bring myself to study them. I hope that with the help of a microscope you, Dr Stre, or you, Lieutenant Hansen, will undertake the task of classification from which I myself have refrained.'

The violent cloudburst had put out all the fires in the zariba, or boma. Nevertheless our cook had been able to complete the preparation of our food under a shelter made of many large leaves. He had used for this purpose a paraffin-stove which had, however, one disadvantage: it made all the cooking-utensils extremely sooty. The result was that all the food he prepared—not least the coffee—had a not altogether agreeable flavour of paraffin.

It went on raining for an unusually long time, and we therefore remained sitting in Sir John's tent for a considerable number of hours. It is true that our own tents were only a few steps away, but despite their fewness we should have been soaked to the skin before we reached cover.

Dr Stre turned to me:

'Some time ago,' he said, 'I expressed the well-founded misgiving that pluvial precipitation would cause our expedition to assume the character of a naval operation. You remember the occasion, sir? I was basing my theory on my knowledge of tropical meteorology, imperfect though it may be.'

He rose and going up to one of the paraffin lamps held one of his cigars in the stream of hot air, meanwhile gently twirling it round between his thumb and forefinger.

'All the same,' I said, 'you were not foresighted enough to store your cigars so that they were protected from the damp.'

'You are both right and wrong, Lieutenant Laronne,' he replied. 'They are packed in tin boxes, carefully soldered, and more resistant to rain and damp than our tent impregnated with copper vitriol. But unfortunately they are outsize boxes. The first few cigars in a newly-opened box are all right, perhaps rather on the dry side, but the later ones are not quite so enjoyable.'

As I said before, Sir John appeared to be in unusually high spirits this evening. He sent for a bottle of Oloroso sherry which he poured out for us after letting it be somewhat cooled by the rain.

'When I was talking about the tent,' he said, 'I lost myself in a series of observations on the subject of fauna, notably insects. I should very much like to offer some further reflections on certain aspects of our marquees.'

He paused while Stre dried his cigar and got it alight.

'I laid emphasis,' he said, 'on the fact that the mosquito-net at the opening of the tent would protect us against flying insects. This protection is, however, very temporary. The net is far too fragile, and it will soon get torn to ribbons. We have reserve nets, but you will soon tire of the everlasting work of repairing them. When they are worn out, it will be practically impossible to have a lighted lamp in the tent.

'I also emphasized,' he continued, 'that beetles, ants, grubs and so on, have a peculiar knack of forcing their way in between the bottom of the tent and the groundsheet. In the not too distant future they will find easier and larger entrances. The canvas on the floor is certainly of very good quality, but that will be of little avail. It will be worn away by the feet of the bed, by projecting roots, that should but have not been removed, by matches carelessly dropped, by your own heels. Here and there we shall certainly be subjected to attacks from a species of ant or beetle which is more enamoured of our tent-canvas than of our provisions. Impregnation appears to act as an appetizer to some of them. Was it copper vitriol you mentioned, Dr Stre?

'On one occasion,' he continued, 'I was ill in bed for forty-eight hours with gastric fever. I don't exclude the possibility that it may have been for seventy-two hours; I was very nearly unconscious. My tent had been pitched in an unsuitable spot and the weather was very warm and damp. I woke up and felt suddenly well again—gastric affections can be of brief duration—and when I sat up in bed I discovered that no less than twenty bamboo shoots had bored their way through the groundsheet. The largest of them was nearly two feet tall.'

'You said something about rain,' said Sir John to Dr Stre, 'about the precipitation we might expect and the character of a naval operation that our expedition would assume.'

'Did you really notice what I said, sir?' asked Stre.

'Of course,' answered our leader, filling up our glasses from the bottle of sherry that had been further chilled by having a wet towel wrapped round it.

'I've been fascinated by rain ever since I was a child,' said Stre. 'Do you regard that as a strange confession, Sir John? You once asserted—it was some weeks ago now—that you had discovered a connection between malaria and wet clothes. I don't wish to dispute your statement, but I should like to take the liberty of saying that I continue to be fascinated by rain, and that to have my clothes glued to my body by moisure gives me a sensation that is almost pleasurable.'

I was well aware that there was no basis for Stre's assertion. He was the only one of us who had sought cover under an umbrella when we encountered thundery showers out on the plains of the Ajanti country. I knew too that among his personal belongings he had at least two spare umbrellas, and that he was also well equipped in the matter of rubber-coated waterproof clothing. I might mention in passing that he had little joy of the latter. In spite of the fact that the rubber had been vulcanized by the most up-to-date methods, the heat made these garments stickier and more adhesive than oilskins.

'The first great travellers,' said Sir John, 'the Portuguese, believed that the earth was divided into five zones. The two zones at its extremities were arctic, and uninhabitable. The central zone was much too hot. Only the two intermediate regions, the temperate zones, were inhabitable by mankind. The central zone was a flaming belt of burning air and boiling water. Consequently, the peoples of the temperate zones could never make contact with one another and were doomed to remain one another's antipodes.'

'We're now in the central zone,' said Stre, 'but the air isn't on fire nor the water boiling and it's raining as if all the floodgates of heaven were opened.'

'Our only difficulty,' said Hansen, 'is to chill the sherry to a civilized temperature.'

Sir John listened politely and patiently and then continued:

'The Portuguese were wrong, we know that now. The belief in a burning fifth zone was not of Portuguese origin but, as far as I know, they never questioned its validity. In spite of this they sailed south. Ship after ship was despatched thither.'

He paused to scrape out his pipe, fill and relight it, and I noticed that the tobacco he had scraped out was not even half smoked.

'What is it you are trying to convey to us, sir?' I asked.

'It is this,' he answered. 'The Portuguese journeys, especially those of Henry the Navigator, provide us with an admirable illustration of the European traveller's morale. He was convinced of the existence of a burning fifth zone, but he did not hesitate to force his way into it.'

'I have a dim recollection,' said Dr Stre, 'that Henry was never on board a ship, at any rate not after it had weighed anchor. Didn't he build a fortress far out on some promontory? And wasn't that fortress shot to pieces by Sir Francis Drake?'

Our conversation was interrupted by a prolonged and violent rumbling, followed by a rapid series of crackling noises. But the rain had stopped and the thunder receded into the far distance. As time went on this auditory experience was repeated at frequent, though irregular, intervals, often many times a day and often after a tempest.

It emanated from the fall of some gigantic tree. The rumbling occurred when its trunk forced a way through the crowns of the lower trees by which it was surrounded, when its many spreading roots broke loose from the soil and when branches and saplings bowed and bent, only to snap a few minutes later.

III

Reveille was sounded at a quarter-past five in the morning, and at six o'clock the advance guard had to be ready to march off.

We had fifteen minutes in which to perform our morning toilet and to see to it that our private belongings were converted into loads. At five-thirty we ate our communal breakfast—which consisted of coffee and biscuits—in the tent that Smitt had christened 'the club-room'. While we were eating breakfast Salaam had the other tents dismantled. It was his men who transported the equipment belonging to the staff of the expedition.

Sir John was now again behaving with the decisiveness and the gravity which appear natural to him, but which contrasted strongly with his lighter mood of the previous evening. He was already seated at the table when I arrived and, in response to a greeting from Lieutenant Hansen, who arrived rather late, he merely remarked briefly that the latter must accept the fact that the coffee was cold.

It was still so dark that we were allowed to have the paraffin lamp alight in the tent.

Sir John told us that at least four Barites had disappeared in the small hours and that we should very likely find more were missing at the fall-in. Two or three men were showing signs of illness, probably dysentery. Their symptoms, however, were not so marked that there was any necessity for an immediate medical examination. That could wait until our midday rest. The sick men had been relieved of their burdens and were temporarily attached to the advance guard.

'You've been very active this morning, sir,' I said. 'Have the deserters taken any stolen goods with them?'

Our leader shook his head. He did not as yet know how matters stood in that respect, but we should no doubt discover at the march past.

'It's obvious,' said Dr Stre, 'that there are some among us who hesitate to force their way into the burning fifth zone, even though they can hardly be aware of its existence.'

The advance guard fell in at six o'clock. Each company had its own bugle-call.

As the men began to march off Uli, the headman of the Ajanti guides, found the body of a dead Galla soldier. He had been pierced through by his three short spears and, to judge by the trampled condition of the moss surrounding him, had been set upon by several people.

Sir John sent for Halmadi, the captain of the askaris. He, however, knew nothing about the incident.

Our leader was upset and annoyed, but did not consider we could delay our departure long enough to hold an investigation and a trial. He told Smitt to see to it that the dead man was buried. Smitt was in charge of the rearguard, and would therefore remain longer in the boma than the rest of us. But Dajatsj would not hand over the burial to the Barites. He had the spears extracted, and the Gallas then carried the dead man with them, so that they could bury him when they had their midday rest.

As soon as the last man in the advance guard had left the camp the fall-in was sounded for the companies of the main body.

IV

During our first march of the day the path grew steadily narrower, and the surrounding vegetation denser. Ten more Ajantis were called to the head of the column to assist with their pangas in the work of removing obstructions, particularly the thorn-covered branches that hung over the path in ever-increasing numbers.

The path forked continually, and was now and then crossed by other paths, all decidedly narrower and clearly less frequently used.

According to information we had received, this part of the forest was supposed to be inhabited by an agricultural people called the Bakvas. We were, however, unable to detect any sign of their existence, if you except the path, which might as well have been made by animals as by men.

At our midday rest Sir John sent for Uli, the Ajanti guide. 'We're on our way east,' he said, 'but for the last hour we've been swinging towards the north. Is the path going to turn eastwards again?'

'I don't know,' answered Uli.

'Where is it leading to?'

'I don't know. The whole forest is full of paths. I take the best one.'

'Where is the nearest Bakva village?'

'I don't know,' answered Uli. 'They are always moving. We cannot be sure that we shall find villages this year in the places where there were villages last year.'

To which Sir John's Indian scribe, our interpreter, added: 'So that is all he knows, and he's the wisest man among us.'

Sir John gave Uli orders that he was to turn off east at the first suitable opportunity, in the hope that we might thus find a path that agreed better with the general direction of our march.

Every Ajanti in the advance guard and ten Galla soldiers, each man equipped with a panga or an axe, were put in the van. The flags of the different companies were furled before we resumed our march. To carry them unfurled was far too impeding and they were in danger of being torn to shreds.

Uli found faint traces of an old path that led in the right direction, and he, and the fifty men he now had to help him, began to chop their way into the forest.

At first our progress was fairly brisk but after a very short time the vegetation grew thicker than ever and the sluggish tempo of our march was further retarded when we reached a vast tangle of rattan lianas.

The soldiers and bearers of the advance guard pressed on

but were overtaken by the main body. Hansen called a halt, but the column was long and the path far too winding for a signal to reach the companies in its rear. It was impossible to prevent their advance and the result was an indescribable crush. Many were squeezed out into the surrounding thickets and many fell and were trampled on. Hansen's gun-bearer lost a shot-gun, which was never recovered.

Our very slow progress unleashed much unrest among the undisciplined pagazis. This was perfectly understandable. For one thing it is tiresome not to be able to march at a steady pace when one is carrying a heavy load, and for another, when they moved slowly, or were forced to stand still, it gave the innumerable black ants an excellent opportunity to attack their bare legs. The unpleasantness of the situation was further increased by the presence of other, tiny ants who lived in the trees and their branches, and who came tumbling down on the men and animals passing beneath them. The people most exposed in this respect were our pioneers, and their bodies were as smothered with tiny blisters as if they had been whipped with stinging nettles.

We had not got far on our afternoon march before Sir John called a halt for the night. The distance we might have covered was further reduced by the unfavourable nature of the ground for making a camp. Much time was required for clearing it and preparing a palisade of bushes. The ground was dangerously damp and it was difficult to clear it because we were now in an area where a tornado had uprooted a large number of giant trees, in all probability in the far distant past.

While we were at work on the boma one of the bearers belonging to Salaam's company was bitten by a snake not more than half a metre long. He succeeded in capturing it, probably because it had been injured by his panga, and came running up to us with his arm outstretched, gripping the snake firmly just behind its head. The species was recognizable by two horn-like protuberances over the eyes. Sir John killed it with a couple of blows from his stick.

Stre gave the Barite an injection of sal volatile and, when this seemed to have no effect, one of potassium permanganate, but within minutes the man was dying in violent convulsions, which Stre tried to alleviate with morphia.

The brother of the victim, one of Salaam's subordinates, asked that the dead man should be buried in a sitting position, facing towards the east. When the grave was dug I was able to take note of a very curious fact. In this most prodigious and luxuriant of forests the layer of soil was no more than ten inches deep at the most, and this despite the fact that the ground was thickly strewn with decaying branches and lianas, rotting leaves and plants. The mould was, moreover, as warm as a compost heap.

Sir John measured the temperature of this layer of humus and found it to be considerably higher than that of the air.

The underlying bed of sand was criss-crossed by isolated roots which were certainly thin, but so tough and hard that they obstinately resisted the blows of the Barite axes.

While the boma was being completed the pioneers continued their attempts to drive a traversable path between and around the gigantic fallen trees. Only a few of these were of the same species, and I left the investigation of them wholly to our leader, or to that well-informed naturalist, Lieutenant Smitt.

The pioneers returned to camp at sunset, but the six Ajanti guides, who had set out to make a longer reconnaissance of the area, did not return until nine o'clock. The manner in which they found their way back in pitch darkness must appear inexplicable to any European.

Uli informed us that he had found a reasonably well-trodden path that led in the right direction.

'How far away is it?' asked Sir John.

Uli replied that he had found the path at sunset and turned back immediately after doing so, and with this estimate of distance we had to be content.

The arms of the six Ajantis were quite badly scratched by thorns and their legs covered with half-dried mud.

Jaffar Topan

Said and I pitched my tent in a corner of the boma. There are corners even in a round boma.

Lieutenant Hansen complained about the rain:

'Heat without sunshine,' he said, 'and then hours of deluging rain. Every day is like every other day. As it has been today, so it will be tomorrow.'

The rain put out all the fires in the boma. Barites, Gallas, and Ajantis crouched under their shelters of large leaves. Those among them who were more experienced builders, and had expended more effort on making their huts, were not much better off than the others.

To Lieutenant Hansen I said:

'There are some people who would hold that you are mistaken, effendim. They would say that a thing can only happen once, that we are always facing what we have never experienced before, and that no one but King Suleiman has seen King Suleiman's sun. It was probably a sufi who said this.'

'What is a sufi?' he asked.

'Suleiman is also called Solomon,' I said.

My tent kept out the rain but the water welled up through the moss that made its floor.

'Do you want to stay here too?' I said to Said.

The boy shook his head.

Kingiri, the captain of No. 2 Company, could not smile; for ever since his childhood the corners of his mouth had been extended by the two slits that curved upwards through his cheeks.

'I have always been going on a journey,' he said. 'I have never stopped anywhere, never dwelt anywhere. On a night like this I understand myself.'

'How large is the forest?' asked Said.

'I do not know,' said Kingiri. 'For many of us it will come to a sudden end.'

Soon after the rain ceased the many fires of the camp were relit. It is hard to make a fire from wet wood. Some people are clever at it, others are not so clever.

The Barites, both askaris and pagazis, used matches, which were dealt out to them sparingly by Kami, the captain of No. 6 Company.

The Galla soldiers struck a light with steel and stone held close to a bit of dried fungus. They use a powder made of the same fungus to stop the flow of blood from a wound.

The Ajantis had brought fire with them in earthenware pots, tiny vessels made of hard shiny earthenware. The necks of these pots were narrow and the bottoms pierced by a number of pin-point holes.

Said asked how large the forest was. We made our way to the Ajanti fires and I repeated his question.

Uli, their headman, answered:

'I do not know of any other end to the forest than the place at which it began.'

'Are you not going to show us the way through the forest?'

He answered that his business was to show us the way to the east, that he had made many long journeys in the forest, that he had always returned to the west, and that the paths grew longer the more people there were travelling together.

'The forest must come to an end in the east too,' said Kingiri.

The copper-helmeted Uli answered:

'There is darkness round the zariba, but in the trees many small men are sitting watching us. It is light in here and they can see us. We cannot see them. They can hear us, but we cannot hear them.'

'How small?' I asked.

'I have bought ivory from them,' answered Uli. 'The tallest of them reach to my heart. Up to now they have only watched us. They can sit on a branch as we pass under it. They can stand behind an ant-hill or the trunk of a tree and let the bearers pass by at arm's length. They are very small. They know that you do not want to buy ivory, and they are afraid of you.'

'Pygmies are swift and agile,' said Said.

Halmadi, the woollen-mantled captain of the askaris, replied:

'The swiftest creature on earth is a sort of one-legged man who, though he has only one leg, can overtake a horse.'

Halmadi was sure there were one-legged men somewhere. He did not know where, but trustworthy people had told stories about them.

'Trustworthy travellers,' said Kingiri, 'have also told stories about men with the heads of dogs. None of these travellers have journeyed more than I have, and I have never seen a man with a dog's head.'

Everyone clustered round the fires now relit after the rain. They beat aside the thick smoke, turned themselves round to dry their clothes, and held out their wet mats and blankets.

Some of them had heard tell of snake-like fishes three hundred feet long. Somewhere too there were gold-mining ants, bigger than jackals, whose treasure no one could get, it was so well hidden, and apart from that, who would want to tackle ants as large as jackals?

There were water-animals who drew down incautious or thirsty elephants with their talons, and held them under water until they were drowned.

One of Salaam's foremen said he did not know whether a manticore, with its blue eyes, its three rows of teeth and its red skin, was a man-like animal or an animal-like man.

And what about those mouthless people who, in spite of their mouthlessness, were far from being ill-nourished, because they could feed on the perfume of flowers and ripe fruit, and whose happiness would have been complete, had it not been for the fact that they instantly died if they were exposed to the least suspicion of a bad smell?

Many people had heard of very large apes who would hide themselves in the brushwood beside the paths and suddenly grab hold of a passer-by's hand and bite off his fingers. And then again there were the felt-eared people. What sort of a creature was a felt-eared man?

One of the Barites who could make himself understood by the Ajantis shouted to Uli:

'What have you done with your little men? Why do they hide from us? Why are they afraid?'

Said curled up by the flap of the tent and therefore, though it was small, there was room in it for six-fingered Kingiri.

I was awakened before daybreak by Said calling out in his sleep. He was very hot. I spread my mat over him and went out of the tent. At one of the two entrances of the boma I heard voices and footsteps. I went closer. The thorny bushes that had blocked the entrance had been partially removed. I shouted a question into the darkness, but received no other answer than the sound of men hastening away.

Laronne

I

It took us a whole day to reach the path that the Ajanti guides had found.

Our departure had been delayed because a further number of our Barite pagazis had deserted and, in doing so, had carried off with them considerably heavier loads than they had previously been capable of bearing. Nine or ten men were reported as having gone down with fever, dysentery or some other gastric affection. We were able to transfer their loads to bearers who no longer had provisions to carry.

We followed Uli's path for two kilometres or so before it was time to camp for the night. The path was fairly wide and straight and the ground firm. Our boma was soon built, owing in no small measure to the fact that Dajatsj's Gallas had now learnt what such a thing should look like.

Two of the men reported sick were missing that evening. Lieutenant Smitt confirmed that in the afternoon he had come upon a Barite sitting by the path, whom the main body had left behind. He had ordered the soldiers of the rear-guard to see to it that the sick man was taken care of and carried if necessary.

'Where is he?' asked Sir John.

Smitt was unable to give any precise information. Sir John ordered the company of askaris forming the rearguard to fall in, but no one knew what had happened to the missing bearer, and it was obvious that no one had taken charge of him.

'Are you sure, Lieutenant Smitt, that you only marched past one sick man?' asked Sir John. 'Two are missing, and,' he added, 'it is one of the duties of the rearguard to ensure that incidents of this kind do not occur.'

At our evening meal Smitt said:

'If you'll allow me, sir, I should like to ask whether you consider that I'm responsible for the disappearance of the two sick Barites.'

'Our losses by desertion are beginning to be disturbing,' replied Sir John. 'The number of men reporting sick is larger than it ought to be. Most of them will soon recover, but we must keep them with us. As long as they can walk they must be forced to march, and if they become completely incapacitated, we have no other alternative but to carry them. We shall not need to resort to this last measure very often. With the help of quinine and a certain amount of pressure a man suffering from a fever can usually continue to walk until he recovers.'

'Neither of the two was suffering from malaria,' said Dr Stre. 'One of them had a troublesome ulcerous infection of the feet and the other was suffering from dysentery. Fortunately there are signs that this is of a fairly mild variety. Dysentery, as you know, is infectious, but,' he added, 'whether the infection is transmitted with the assistance of miasma or of Koch's bacteria is another matter.'

When Dr Stre had finished speaking, Smitt resumed:

'You never answered my question, Sir John. You marshalled the whole of Halmadi's company and questioned the men about the missing Barites. This took a considerable time. It held up the work on the boma and delayed our evening meal. You could just as well have questioned Halmadi and his subordinates. You have made quite a fuss about the whole affair.'

Our leader regarded Smitt for a long time. He had seated himself in an easy chair and lit his pipe. Along one jaw ran a smudge of dry shaving-soap, left when he had performed his hasty preprandial toilet. None of us would have dreamt of drawing his attention to this, nor did it rob him of a tittle of his dignity.

'You express yourself with a frankness that I appreciate, Smitt,' he said at last.

'On two previous occasions,' said Smitt, 'you have made remarks which suggest that you are not completely satisfied with me. If you wish, I am quite prepared to tender my resignation and go back.'

'The work on the boma was not held up by the inquiry,' replied Sir John. 'The camp was ready when you arrived with the rearguard, Lieutenant Smitt. That, however, is a minor matter. The idea that I might want you and the expedition to part company is entirely without foundation.

'There is something very interesting about your suggestion,' he continued. 'You talk about tendering your resignation. Far too many Barites have already deserted during the nights. You talk of resigning. It is very interesting.'

Dr Stre, who had just dried one of his cigars in the warm air circulating above the paraffin lamp and then puffed several large clouds of smoke into the quantities of butterflies and moths that were fluttering round it, now spoke:

'I should be grateful, sir, if you could explain precisely what it is you consider interesting. Won't you please do so?'

'I have a friend,' said Sir John, 'whose name is Hamed bin Mohammed bin Juma. He is an Arab, as you may have gathered from his long and difficult name. It is perhaps a mistake to call him my friend, but we know one another well. He claims that he is a descendant of Tamar the Lame, a circumstance which, of course, in some ways contradicts the statement that he is an Arab.

'This Hamed,' he continued, 'has made more and perhaps longer journeys than I have. On his return he has always rendered thanks to Allah for letting him return alive, and for saving him from being killed or deserted by his Arab officers.'

'But you, sir,' said Stre, 'run no risk of being killed or deserted by your officers.'

'Precisely. You may possibly consider handing in your resignation, but if this is not accepted you will loyally stand by your original undertaking. That is what is interesting, and it is as good an example as any of the difference between a European and a non-European.'

'Can't you count on the same loyalty from Dajatsj and the Gallas?' asked Hansen.

'Not quite,' answered Sir John. 'All the same there is a difference between them and our Barite askaris. They were selected by British officers, and for many years they have been carefully drilled under British command.'

II

A further number of Barites were missing in the morning and still more had gone down with dysentery. Dr Stre's view that the illness was manifesting itself in a mild form was confirmed by the fact that those who had sickened first were now well enough to resume their places in their respective companies.

On this morning the food-ration had to be somewhat reduced in comparison with what had been issued ever since we left Fort John. This had amounted to about a pound of bread made of arrowroot or manioc, and about the same amount of rice, maize- or wheat-flour per man per day.

Because of the number of deserters and sick, Sir John and Stre stayed behind in the camp to inspect the main body, while I marched ahead with our advance guard of Ajantis, Gallas, and Sjimba's No. 4 Company of bearers.

The path led over reasonably firm ground. Other paths joined it, thereby increasing its width and hardness, but the surrounding vegetation became simultaneously denser. It rather looked as if the additional air-space created by the path had stimulated the growth of saplings, lianas, brushwood and ferns.

Only a few metres from the spot where we had taken our midday siesta the head of the column came to a halt. On the path, side by side, lay a dead man and a dead woman. They had not yet been attacked by insects, so they could only just have been killed.

'There is no mistaking the meaning of this,' said Sir John's scribe and interpreter.

'What do you mean?' I asked.

'They are lying on their faces,' he answered. 'They are lying as if, when they were killed, they were walking in the same direction as ourselves. Can you mistake the meaning of that, effendim?'

The dead people were dark-skinned and quite unlike the Ajantis in appearance.

Less than an hour later the Ajantis again came to a halt. Ahead the path opened out into a broad track, five paces wide, that had been cut through the forest. This track was perhaps five hundred feet in length and ended at a village composed of many tall huts. In front of the village, at the place where the track ended, a very large number of bowmen were assembled.

There was a stream close to the village, rather narrow it is true, but wide enough to separate the tree-tops and produce a gap that let in air and sunshine. We had come from the green half-light. The village and the bowmen were as brightly illuminated as if they had been a stage set, complete with wings and a multitude of supers.

'Why have you stopped, Uli?' I asked the Ajantis' headman.

'The road is far too wide,' answered Sir John's scribe.

I asked if they were afraid of the bowmen, but the Indian interpreter replied:

'The Ajantis are more afraid for their feet.'

Uli lifted up the moss and leaves with his panga and revealed wooden skewers driven into the ground. He pulled one out and gave it to me. It was about a foot long and the projecting end was as sharp as an awl. The other end was cleft to make it hold more firmly in the ground. The skewer had been cut from a very hard kind of wood. It felt like horn and had deep red streaks in it. Smitt later asserted that it was probably some kind of ebony.

The whole of the wide track was studded with these skewers, hidden under moss, leaves and twigs.

Twelve Ajantis were told to creep forward in a line removing the skewers as they went. Behind them came a group of Gallas, their rifles at the ready, and these were soon joined by more as others came pouring out of the narrow path and spread across the width of the track.

We moved forward in silence and the bowmen waited in silence.

When we had got less than half way, a shower of arrows was discharged. Distance obliged the bowmen to aim upwards and their arrows described high arcs in the air. Few of them reached us and no one was hit.

Nearly a hundred Gallas fired, reloaded and fired again. It was impossible to stop them before the forty men among them armed with Winchesters had emptied their magazines.

The tight cluster in which the men of the village had been standing was broken up in a few seconds.

III

The skewers in the ground held us up and we did not reach the village until Sir John had arrived with the main body.

'Was this necessary?' he asked.

'They shot at us,' I replied, 'and the Gallas retaliated with their rifles.'

'Did you try to negotiate?' he asked.

'I never got near enough, sir,' I answered.

A wounded youth was taken prisoner. He had been hit in the shoulder and had a large lump on his forehead, which might have been caused by a ricochet, though it is not impossible that the injury to his forehead had been there before we arrived.

We were able to communicate with him through Sir John's scribe and interpreter, who in his turn was helped by Uli, the headman of the Ajantis.

'Why did you try to stop us from advancing?' I asked.

'Why have you come here?' replied the prisoner. 'Why did you kill us?'

'Tomorrow we shall march on towards the east.'

'You were marching towards our village.'

'Why did you plant skewers in our road?'

'He says that it is their road,' Sir John's scribe told me. 'The skewers were not planted in our road but in their road.'

We pitched our tents in the centre of the Bakva village. It was a small place and the deserted huts were neither large enough nor numerous enough to house all our men. It was surrounded by a palisade of widely spaced stakes around which had been planted a wide hedge of thorn bushes.

The Bakvas who had been killed were laid in rows on the track they themselves had cleared. We did not bury them. We were moving on next day and Sir John considered that the best thing to do was to leave the dead to their surviving relatives, as we knew nothing of their burial customs.

The Bakva village had not much to offer in the way of provisions. On the maize patches green stalks were showing. The red tubers of the manioc were still far too small and bitter and the plantains had flowers but no fruit. Our Bakva prisoner told us that there had been famine over a wide area for a long time.

While the dead were being carried out of the village one of our Gallas managed to tread on a skewer that had been overlooked. The point entered his foot just in front of the heel, passed between all the bones and tendons of the ankle and was just visible under the skin of the lower part of his shin. Only a few minutes elapsed before the soldier was treated by Dr Stre, but he had already begun to display symptoms which clearly indicated poisoning. He was delirious to the verge of unconsciousness, he had a very rapid pulse, he was sweating profusely, and the swollen and inflamed condition of his foot could not be explained by the wound in itself.

Stre applied appreciable quantities of sal volatile under the skin on both sides of the foot and by the bone in front. It proved impossible to extract the skewer except by making an incision by its point and drawing it through the foot with a pair of pincers. The operation was a painful one for the injured man in spite of the fact that he was only semi-conscious and had been given an injection of morphia before it started.

An inspection of the skewers that had been pulled up revealed that they were all smeared with a reddish-yellow substance, which might at first glance easily escape detection because of the red stripes in the wood.

IV

After our evening meal, a fairly spartan repast consisting of meat broth, dry bread, and a tin of preserved fruit, Salaam, the captain of No. 1 Company, and Halmadi, the captain of the Barite soldiers, presented themselves.

When Sir John asked them what they wanted, they explained that the Barites were loudly complaining about the provisions with which they had been furnished, and that many of them showed a marked decline in weight and strength.

'We have been obliged to cut down the daily ration,' answered Sir John, 'and we shall be obliged to reduce it still further tomorrow and probably on the following days too, unless we succeed in replenishing our stocks.'

'Many will greet with joy the news that the ration is to be reduced,' said Salaam. 'They are already quite sick of cassava-bread and rice.'

Halmadi added:

'There were some tens of goats left behind in the village. They were seized by the Gallas, and all that is left of them now is bones, horns, hair, and hooves.'

'They are also complaining about the rain,' said Salaam.

'They are also asking how long the road is that we must travel before we reach the Pasha,' added Halmadi.

'Tell your men that I too am tired of rice and cassava,' replied Sir John. 'The same rain that falls on them falls on me too. As for the road to the Pasha, they themselves will determine how long it is to be.'

Jaffar Topan

Said said to Uli:

'Where are your pygmies? The dead men are as tall as we are.'

'The dead men are Bakvas, not pygmies,' answered the Ajanti guide.

'You spoke of pygmies who sat in the trees around us and watched us.'

'They are there.'

'Where?'

Uli pointed with his rifle. He let the butt rest on the ground and swung the upward-pointing muzzle round in a circle.

'There. They are very small and agile. They can see us; we cannot see them. They hear us; we do not hear them.'

'I have always been a traveller,' said Kingiri. 'I have always been on my way somewhere. I am old.'

He was sitting on his mat with his legs drawn up under him. He was in a half-reclining position, resting on one elbow to avoid touching the wet side of the tent.

'I shall light my pipe this evening,' he said. 'It is long since I last did so. Who would want to stay here? We are on our way, no one wants to stay here. Where does anyone want to stay?'

'It is too warm here,' said Said, the boy from Amman, who was wrapped in his mat.

'He is already asleep,' I said. 'You do not remember where you were born, Kingiri?'

He shook his absurd little head.

'You must have been born somewhere?'

He had lit his pipe and was smoking it with slow, deep inhalations.

'My first memory is of the Arabs,' he said. 'It was a morning and cold. I was walking but I grew tired and someone carried me, or possibly I was allowed to ride, perhaps on a donkey. Children grow up and become valuable. You do not leave them behind. There were very many of us on that first, cold morning that I remember. I seldom smoke.'

The Gallas, as part of the advance guard, had secured the best huts for themselves. The askaris, the soldiers of the rearguard, had arrived last and there were far too few huts. In the Bakva village there were no trees with leaves large enough to build even the humblest shelter.

They began to fight each other as soon as Sir John and his lieutenants had put out the lights in their tents. They did not stop until Laronne separated them.

A few hours later arrows and some isolated spears began to fall on our camp.

An arrow that falls from a height loses its force. It may penetrate the canvas of a tent, but it sticks in the roof of a hut. A spear falling from a height keeps its weight even in its fall, but it seldom hits anything as it is thrown at random.

Uli was awake. His copper helmet gleamed in the light of a fading fire.

'These are Bakva spears and Bakva arrows,' he said.

'Where are we going?' he, our guide, asked me.

'Towards the east,' I answered.

'There are many who will turn back tonight or when day begins to break,' he said. 'I have seen them getting ready.

They are whispering to each other and they have prepared their loads.'

'Many?' I asked.

'A great many or not so many,' he answered. 'It is dark. How should I know?'

'It is dark and hot,' I said. 'I have a tent in which a sick youth, not much more than a child, is sleeping. Kingiri is there too, smoking hemp.'

'Those who are thinking of turning back, they will not get far,' said the headman of the Ajantis. 'They know nothing about the forest. You can never find your way back by the same road in the forest. Who is Kingiri?'

The village lay close to a river. It was narrow and flowed slowly from the east. Just above the village it became two rivers. The main stream flowed from the north. The arm that flowed from the east was too shallow and too twisting to allow us to use the boats that were being carried by the company whose captain was called Abdul the Ninety-ninth.

For three days we followed this arm of the river along a well-trodden path. We could have marched quite a lot faster, if it had not been that the men clearing the way were obliged to widen the path, simply to make room for Abdul's boat-bearers, as the sections into which the boats were divided were three feet across, and the path, though well-trodden, was narrow.

We saw the river, or rather the arm that flowed from the east, many times each day. It was now no longer broad enough to prevent the tree-tops on one bank from mingling with the tree-tops on the other. The river, like the path, was now a tunnel.

The days were gloomily green, the nights unbelievably dark.

*

Uli and his five guides walked in front. They continually came to a standstill, sank upon their knees and pulled out one of the poisoned skewers from the ground.

These skewers, the arrows of the earth, were not thick on the ground, but they were there, cleverly hidden under moss and leaves. Some of them, like the first we had encountered, were dipped in bright red poison. Most were smeared with a black substance.

Wherever a fallen tree lay across our path, we could be sure that we should find a large number of skewers at the spot where we should be most likely to tread when choosing the easiest place to climb over the tree-trunk.

The path often forked and, as we were marching along the right-hand side of the river, Uli always chose the left-hand fork.

Halmadi, the mournful woollen-mantled captain of the Barite soldiers, complained: 'Why do we always turn to the left?'

'For many reasons,' I answered.

'These who turn to the left,' he said, 'what men are these? Yes, they are those who are exposed to suffocating winds and scalding water and shade cast by black smoke that does not cool or refresh them. That too is written.'

We passed through more than twelve villages, all exactly like the first. No one tried to stop us any more. The Bakvas would often linger there until we were less than a hundred paces from the opening of the palisade. Then we would halt and send ahead our Bakva prisoner, whom we had named Mali, to speak well of us, but the villages would be empty when we marched into them.

Before we sent Mali ahead we fastened a long flexible rope to one of his legs.

We spent the night in three of these villages. They were

certainly small, but round them were thorny defences and we were spared the labour of making our own boma.

We found very little in the way of food. It was the wrong season, and there was nothing to be gathered on the patches of cultivation.

Every night fighting broke out between the Gallas and the Barites. Laronne, the vakeel, was always the first person to intervene and separate them. He had cut himself a new rattan switch. One night—the fires had gone out and it was very dark—he was obliged to defend himself, and in doing so killed a Barite and wounded two Gallas.

Halmadi said:

'The Gallas march in front. No one wishes to deprive them of the right to sleep in the huts they have chosen for themselves. Who would want to sleep under the same roof as a Galla?'

And Kingiri answered:

'No one wants to sleep in the same hut as a Galla. Who would want to do that? I am not afraid of them. I am too old to be afraid of anything.'

'The Galla soldiers march in front,' said Halmadi. 'The village will be empty of people, but have you never smelt anything when the Gallas roast goats or perhaps sheep that did not manage to get away? And what is this?' he continued, holding out a fistful of feathers. 'Have you ever seen a feathered goat or a sheep with wings? And have not you yourself eaten nothing but dry cassava bread since you know not when?'

'The goats are few,' I said, 'the hens fewer. There comes a point beyond which it is much too difficult to share.'

The captain of the askaris answered:

'That those who are well off must share their abundance, of that there is no doubt. The meaning of the text is unmistakable. But it is also stated that the man whose lot is humble shall share with others that which Allah has bestowed on him in short measure. And if a man reaches the point where it is no longer possible to share, then he can abstain from that which is indivisible. This is written in the sura called Divorce, or the sura called Prohibition. I find it difficult to keep apart the last fifty suras. They are brief, but they are many.'

'And is that the reason?' I asked.

'It is difficult to stop those who in this way are left with nothing,' said Halmadi. 'It is also written that Allah permits alleviation to follow hardship. But it does not say whether alleviation comes of itself, or whether it must be seized by force.'

At night Bakva spears and Bakva arrows fell upon our camp. Only one man, a Barite, was hit. A spear fell through the roof of a hut so unluckily that it went through the man's upper arm, the skin of his stomach and his left thigh. He was sleeping curled up and was pinned fast to the ground. No one heard him and he was dead by morning.

'Where are your pygmies?' we asked Uli.

'All round us and above us,' he answered.

'The people we have seen so far are as big as we are.'

'It is the pygmies who make the poison,' he said, 'both the yellow poison and the black. They can talk to one another above our heads. They whistle to each other. We do not hear them. They whistle to each other when they want to be inaudible. You must have a pygmy's ears to hear a pygmy's whistle.'

We spent two nights in the third Bakva village. The intervening day was a rest-day. Laronne and Hansen, accompanied by a guard of Ajantis and Gallas, went off on a hunting expedition.

The Barites complained of the increasing scarcity of food, and the ever-decreasing rations of cassava, rice, and flour. The mournful woollen-mantled Halmadi was always reminding himself of what had been written, and said that nothing else was to be expected. Had it not been clearly stated that no man should enter a stranger's house before he had asked permission and given the owners a greeting? Had we not sinned against this law? The cabins of the Bakva people were small and dirty, but they must still be regarded as dwellings. And ought we not to turn back when we were told to do so? The words of the Prophet were unequivocal. Therefore, what else but misfortune could come upon us?

Nevertheless the huntsmen managed to shoot a number of buffaloes. They returned to the camp blowing their bugles and were greeted by salvoes, let off into the air by the Gallas.

Sir John chose what he wanted, and Said's men cut up the rest. Dajatsj and Hansen divided the meat into nine heaps, one for each company and one for the Ajantis.

The Galla captain called up the leaders of each company, one by one, and pointed with his bundle of spears:

'Here is yours,' he said. 'Do not forget that each man must have his share. You can eat with a clear conscience, this is the flesh of buffalo, not of swine. Do not forget to chew before you swallow! Do not fight over the bags and the balls, Barites! We well know you all need them, but those who are strongest need them least. Therefore do not fight, brothers!'

Another man who took part in the distribution was the Galla foreman known as Five Pounds. He was the man who had been injured by the sharp handle of Laronne's rattan switch. The wound, which had originally been superficial, had gone gangrenous, spread outwards, and become so deep that there would soon be a hole between the muscles of his calf and the actual shin-bone.

'Have you never consulted our doctor?' I asked.

He shook his head.

'I can still walk,' he said.
'It will get worse.'
'Yes.'
'It may end badly for you.'
'I know who it was that gave me the wound,' he replied.

Laronne

I

The large number of desertions occasioned us a great deal of concern.

Speaking of them our leader said:

'You may perhaps recall that at the start I was able to treat the desertions with a certain nonchalance. I talked of a process of selection, and said that those who deserted first were the ones who would have caused us trouble later on.'

'Your argument was attractive, sir,' said Stre.

'The position is now reversed,' said Sir John. 'It is still a question of a process of selection, but the men who desert now are the strongest and most daring. The others dare not, or haven't the strength.'

The desertions usually took place at night, probably as near daybreak as possible, and they really did require daring and determination on the part of the deserters, particularly in this Bakva country, where our camp was in continual danger from poisoned arrows and spears.

We increased the number of guards on night-duty. These sentries were told that they must not only keep an eye on what was happening outside the camp, they must also be watchful of what might be going on inside it. The deserters were almost all pagazis. No Galla soldier had absconded so far, and only a few of the askaris, our Barite soldiers. The Ajantis too were reliable.

'The Ajantis don't feel the need to desert,' said Sir John's scribe. 'Or it may be possible that they haven't yet found any reason for wanting to return home. They are less afraid of the forest than the Barites, and they know that they can find their way back when they please. They will therefore follow us as long as they want to, effendim.'

On one occasion Smitt proposed that we should abandon the smallest boat, thus relieving a number of pagazis from No. 7 Company for other duties. The total number of steel boat-sections was forty-nine, and each one required two bearers.

Our leader emphatically rejected the proposal.

'The boats have so far been little more than a nuisance,' said Smitt. 'Up to now we have had no use for them.'

'What do you know of the use we are likely to have for them in future, Lieutenant Smitt?' asked Sir John.

'I admit,' answered Smitt, 'that I know no more about that than you do, sir.'

The heat and the humidity were very oppressive, but it was again demonstrated that I found it easier to stand up to this kind of ordeal than did Hansen, Smitt, and Stre. Indeed, I was sometimes inclined to think that my powers of endurance were greater than those of our leader.

The day after we left the last Bakva village the river swung southwards and we were obliged to cross it. It was wide enough to cause us considerable difficulty, but not wide enough to provide us with a reason for assembling the boats. At the spot where we forded it we found the remains of a recently destroyed suspension bridge.

The men who first stormed this watercourse were subjected to fierce onslaughts from some kind of ringed worms of varying sizes, which fastened on to their skin and bit holes in it with their sharp jaws. It appeared, however, that there were only a limited number of them, and the succeeding companies got across without being attacked. The vegetation close to the river also proved to be the habitat of an insect—according to Smitt some species of tick—which burrowed under the skin and caused severe pain. It was so minute that at first it was almost invisible, but after a few hours it swelled up and turned red. The largest example—secured by Stre and handed over to Smitt—was half an inch long and a good quarter of an inch in diameter.

'I am beginning to appreciate,' said Stre, 'the view held by our revered leader, that it is unsuitable for a European to indulge in even a modicum of nakedness in a tropical environment.'

II

Four bearers belonging to Sjimba's company deserted. Each man took his Snider with him and between them they had a total of four hundred cartridges. They also took twenty pounds of brass, a fairly large roll of cloth, and one of our last remaining bags of biscuits.

Their flight took place just before sunrise, when there was already a faint hint of daylight. They were seen by the Gallas, who fired shots in their direction, but failed to hit anyone.

They lost their way in the dense vegetation. They had taken rifles but no pangas, a characteristic action for Barites. A panga implies the heavy work of chopping your way through. If you have no pangas you avoid the labour of chopping.

They first fled towards the south, but must later have unintentionally turned east. Then—in spite of the fact that they could not see the sun—they must have begun to doubt if they were going in the right direction, so they tried turning north. In doing so they came upon the path along which our main body had just passed. They followed this path westwards and soon ran into our rearguard.

The meeting took place at a point where the green walls of the path were exceptionally thick. They were seized by Halmadi's soldiers, disarmed, and put into fetters, which were, however, slack enough to make it possible to force each of them to carry a man's load in addition to the stolen goods he had already. They were put at the head of the column and, as they were tired even before they were caught, they delayed the arrival of the rearguard at the place where we were camping for the night.

Smitt went to Sir John's tent to report that he had seized and brought back the four deserters. Sir John was just engaged in having a wash and a shave and in changing his clothes, so they talked through the canvas of the tent. He issued orders that the men were to be carefully bound and guarded by Gallas.

At our evening meal Hansen asked what he intended to do with the four captives.

'We shall be obliged to make an example of them,' said Sir John. 'We can't tolerate any more desertions.'

'What sort of an example, sir?' asked Hansen.

'We shall sentence them in collaboration with the captains of the companies,' he answered. 'We and they will decide the matter together. It will be done later this evening.'

'How extensive do you think the forest is?' asked Hansen.

'Unfortunately I'm not certain of the distance we've covered up to now,' replied Sir John. 'I've not much more than my pedometer to guide me. It has been impossible ever since we left the Ajanti plain to establish our position with the assistance of more reliable nautical instruments. As you have probably noticed, the sun has not been available for taking measurements of angular distances.'

'But, sir!' exclaimed Lieutenant Hansen, 'have you no idea at all of how big the forest is? Our Dutch host at Port Prim showed us some maps, and those are the only maps I have seen.'

Sir John remained silent while Said, his servant from Amman, poured out coffee for the second time. Our leader's trousers were strikingly well-pressed, and this evening he was not wearing boots, but white canvas shoes. To judge by a faint odour he had been anointing his feet with tincture of iodine, a supposition confirmed by the fact that close to the soles the shoes were somewhat discoloured.

At last he said:

'When making my journeys, Lieutenant Hansen, I have learnt that maps and experience do not always correspond. This applies especially to maps of areas that have never been explored.'

III

The eight captains presented themselves and sat down in a semicircle in front of our dining-tent, our club-house, as Hansen—or maybe it was Smitt—had christened it.

Said and Sir John's Indian scribe had built a splendid fire upon which they threw twigs from a tree, the wood of which blazed up in tall, white flames, producing a light-effect that reminded one of acetylene lamps.

The four prisoners were led forward by their Galla guards. Barite and Galla soldiers assembled on the outer edge of the circle of light.

After our leader had exchanged his canvas shoes for boots, we also took our places opposite the leaders of the various companies. Sir John made a short speech in which he dealt with the intolerable heat, the depth of the forest, the poisoned arrows and skewers, the enemies who surrounded us, the shortage of food, the many snakes and insects, and the necessity of winning our way through the forest, and on to our goal.

He asked:

'If anyone shoots at us with poisoned arrows, haven't we the right to shoot him?'

The captains nodded.

'If anyone tries to cut our throats while we sleep, haven't we the right to kill him?'

'Yes,' answered Halmadi.

'Aren't our weapons the only protection we have against those who try to kill us?'

All the eight captains nodded.

'Hasn't the man who deserts us and takes our weapons with him also tried to kill us?'

'You are right, sir,' said Salaam, the captain of No. 1 Company.

'Is Salaam right?' asked Sir John.

'Yes,' answered the captains.

'So you have sentenced these four men to death,' said Sir John. 'They will be hanged, one early tomorrow morning, the second on the following morning, the third on the morning after that, and the fourth on the fourth morning.'

Jaffar Topan

When we left the Bakva villages behind us we were no longer subjected to nightly attacks from arrows and spears, but we again had the arduous task of clearing a boma every evening. We were still following a path, but the distance between the poisoned skewers grew greater.

The forest became even denser, though no one could have imagined a forest denser than the one through which we had already passed.

Our daily ration of food decreased.

Said grew steadily thinner, and his sleep more disturbed, more broken by fits of sweating and violent tossing. He often gave loud cries, though this did not mean that he was awake. Kingiri slept heavily.

A very violent storm of rain fell upon us. It was not preceded by thunder or wind and it was unlike earlier rainstorms in being cold.

That night, Dajatsj, the Galla captain, slept outside my tent. He lay on his side with his knees drawn up and let the rain fall on him. He held his rifle and his three spears in a firm grip. He breathed deeply and quietly and slept with his mouth shut, perfectly relaxed, if you discount the jerking of his calves and forearms occasioned by mosquitoes, ants and other small, crawling things.

The unusually cold rain fell all night. Before daybreak I was awakened by Halmadi, the Syrt, a people of whom no one has ever heard. He climbed over Said and sat down between me and Kingiri. He was shivering with cold and his wet woollen mantle smelt unpleasantly. I lit my lamp and drew the opening of the tent together again. Light at night attracts many things. Mosquitoes and flies were whirling round us and beetles were hurling themselves against the canvas like things possessed.

The lamp radiated warmth, the tent was small.

'I have learnt,' said Halmadi, 'that there are no great events. All events are small.'

'But the night is cold,' I said. 'Is not this our first cold night?'

'A cold night is a small event. There are only small events. Not even the Prophet experienced any but small events, but they were many.'

'Dajatsj is sleeping outside the tent,' I said. 'Cold rain does not trouble the Gallas.'

I gave Halmadi a piece of maize-bread. He took it without looking at me and ate, chewing each bite for a long time. With one foot he pushed Kingiri nearer the side of the tent and settled himself more comfortably.

'It is the same with Kaaba,' he continued. 'Kaaba is not a great event. Kaaba is built of thousands upon thousands of small bricks. Do you understand? You can creep round the temple on your knees and it seems a great building, but it is composed only of many small bricks that have been fitted together.'

'I have never been to Mecca,' I answered. 'But I have seen mosques that are larger than the building called Kaaba.'

'They too have been built of small bricks,' answered Halmadi, the woollen-mantled captain of the Barites; 'and,' he added, 'it would be well if men could eat bricks.'

I gave him another piece of maize-bread.

'It would be well if men could eat bricks,' he repeated. 'A brick can lie in water for three hundred years without disintegrating. I believe it was Hasan from Basra who said this.'

Four deserters had been taken prisoner and were going to be executed. They had been sentenced to death and were to be hanged in the course of four days, one each morning.

Morning came after the cold rain. The Gallas' bugler sounded the fall-in and the other buglers echoed his signal. Beside the entrance to the boma through which we were going to march stood a tree with a suitable branch.

The four prisoners could not agree which of them should die first. Sir John made them draw lots. He gave Dajatsj four matches to hold out to them, three of equal length and the fourth short.

The short match was drawn by the youngest of them. He was called Abdul, like so many other Barites.

They had forgotten to have a rope in readiness, and there was a pause while they searched for one in the baggage. It was thrown over the branch of the tree, and a noose was put round Abdul's neck.

Sir John asked if he had anything to say. He could not answer and fell to the ground in a heap.

Dajatsj was given orders to hoist the doomed man aloft, but the Galla captain answered:

'We are soldiers, sir. We will shoot those who want to kill us, but we will not hang a bound man.'

The three other prisoners were told to haul Abdul up. They obeyed, but the rope did not slip easily over the rough branch. Abdul's hands were bound in front of him, but not firmly enough to stop him seizing the rope above his head and heaving himself up by his arms, all the while emitting loud cries. Several Barites rushed forward to help the three prisoners and thus bring to an end what was happening.

Abdul was hoisted up hanging by his arms. He was light and possessed of convulsive strength. He went on shouting.

Lieutenant Smitt ran towards his tent. He was stopped by Dajatsj's second-in-command, the man called Five Pounds, who gave him his rifle. Smitt fired twice at Abdul, though the latter's hands fell from the rope after the first shot.

We were short of rope and Sir John did not want to leave behind the length with which Abdul had been hanged. After it had been replaced by a stout rope of lianas the dead man was again hoisted up. As the branch stretched across the exit from the boma all the companies had to pass under him as they marched out.

The forest was full of birds. Most of them we could only hear. They lived in the tree-tops and we never saw them. The birds under the green roof were all very tiny, many of them smaller than the largest butterflies. It is most unlikely that vultures and kites ever found their way down into the forest.

I said to Said:

'He is hanging in the air, but he will nevertheless be the prey of ants. They were in the lianas before they were twisted together, not the little red ants, but the big black ones that usually stay on the ground.'

Close to a small stream the Galla soldiers had a sharp exchange of shots with a large group of natives, who soon retreated and vanished into the greenery. Five Gallas were hit by arrows. One of them died as he was being carried to Dr Stre; two of the others were dead next morning.

The natives who had been killed had darker skins than Mali, our Bakva prisoner, but they were the same height.

'Where are your pygmies?' we asked Uli. 'Where are your very small, agile men?'

'They are all round us,' he answered, as he had answered so many times before. 'They see us, we do not see them.

They fear us. It is they who make the poison for the arrows, both the black and the bright red.'

It was unendurably hot at midday. The air lost its transparency. Heat oozed out of the leafy roof above our heads. The silence round us deepened.

You do not only hear with your ears. Treading on a large beetle is like crushing a head, but you hear the crunch of it with your heels not with your ears.

You may go deaf without losing your ears or your hearing. Even very loud noises may be drowned and obliterated by great heat.

We marched on without a midday rest in spite of the heat. The path was more of a tunnel than it had ever been, and the ground spongy with moisture, but we could find no water to drink.

After some hours the forest darkened as if night had already fallen. We heard no thunder or wind, but cold rain poured down on us, so icy cold that the chill of the preceding evening seemed no more than an omen, and the memory of it faded and was lost.

The darkness forced us to clear a space for our camp immediately.

I pitched my tent between two gigantic fallen trees. I had to do this without Said's help. Very soon after the main body arrived at the boma, Kingiri found the boy from Amman lying under the leaves of a cluster of tree-like ferns. The stems of these ferns were so thick and tough that they had defied the blows of the pangas and been left as they were.

Kingiri carried him to my tent. He was sleeping heavily and very restlessly and even the cold rain had been unable to cool his body.

I went to find Dr Stre and he returned with me to Said

after he had put on his waterproof clothing. It was not easy to find our way across the boma. It was pitch dark. Those of the men who had not huddled together where there was some shelter were running hither and thither. All efforts to make a fire had failed. We collided first with Lieutenant Smitt and then with Laronne, and both came with us.

Stre examined the boy and then gave him some medicine.

Laronne, our leader's vakeel, asked me:

'Whose is the tent?'

'Mine, sir,' I answered.

'Have you your own tent?'

'I have had it ever since we left Port Prim,' I answered. 'Haven't you seen it before, effendim? Every night?'

'Do you carry it yourself?'

'Haven't you seen it before?' I asked. 'It is a good tent, but the opening will not close very tightly. It is better not to have a lighted lamp in it, effendim. All these insects!'

'Who gave you permission?'

'Who forbade me, sir?'

Kingiri lifted Said up and I laid his mat under him folded in four. Kingiri, the captain of No. 2 Company, wrapped his own mat round him.

'What has happened to your hand?' asked Smitt. Dr Stre and Laronne had gone but Smitt still sat in the opening of the tent holding up the paraffin lamp.

He took hold of Kingiri's left wrist. Of his left hand only the thumb and a bare half of the palm was left.

'What happened?' he repeated.

'It was a long time ago,' answered Kingiri. 'Now I am very old. Look at my face and my arms. And my mouth, effendim.'

Smitt let go of his hand.

'The boy who stole the pearls,' he asked. 'What happened to him?'

'In Bari harbour?' I asked. 'The thief you caught?'

Kingiri crept to the back of the tent.

'What do you know?' I asked him, but to Smitt I said:

'Kingiri knows nothing. Allah punishes those He wishes to punish, and forgives those He wishes to forgive. He is also called al-Rahman, the lenient and merciful.'

'I am no Muslim,' I said and added: 'The flesh of children and young people heals easily, effendim.'

Laronne

I

We surprised an elephant rolling in a shallow, slimy pool. Uli, the headman of the Ajanti guides, and one of the Gallas each fired two shots. They could not have missed him, but the elephant vanished into the brushwood, saplings, and lianas. We were unable to find any traces of blood, and Sir John considered that pursuit would be futile.

The elephant was quite a large one, and must have had on him more than seven thousand pounds of meat and edible entrails.

Less than half an hour later we found the remains of two elephants. They were lying close together. The flesh had almost all been removed, and swarms of ants and flies had settled on the skeletons. Uli brought us some arrows to look at, five in all, and assured us that they were what had killed the elephants. These arrows were not tipped with metal, but they were as sharp as needles. On each were a number of shallow, spiral grooves, intended no doubt to catch and hold the poison in which the arrows had been dipped. This poison was black. It had a curious smell, and felt sticky to the touch.

Dr Stre and Smitt examined both the poison used on the arrows, and the black and yellow, or rather copal-coloured, poison with which the treacherous skewers had been impregnated. Both types, regardless of colour, could at times be met with as a sticky substance, not unlike gum in consistency, at others as a hard, shiny varnish.

The soft poison—presumably fresher than the hard one—dissolved almost immediately in water. The hard poison flaked off rather slowly, but the process was accelerated if the water was warmed.

The constituents of the poison, however, evaded both Stre's and Smitt's attempts at analysis and definition.

'The smell of asafoetida is unmistakable,' said the doctor. 'It is faint, but it is there. Asafoetida is still used in some places as an antispasmodic. The effect of the poison, notwithstanding its smell, is of a radically different character.'

Our remedies were simple, consisting of injections of sal volatile in conjunction with an emetic. The result was satisfactory, especially if the treatment could be given immediately, and if the poison was of the hard, shiny variety.

'Fernandez, one of the first great travellers, knew the right antidote,' said Sir John. 'It was called theriac, and was composed of no less than sixty-seven different ingredients. Fernandez was one of the men sent out by Henry the Navigator.'

II

Heavy rain compelled us to pitch camp early. Sir John had us all called to his tent. He had changed his clothes, but not yet washed or shaved. He was wearing a clean white shirt, unbuttoned at the neck, with the sleeves rolled up.

'Is there any reason,' he asked, 'why the four deserters should not all have been hanged at once instead of one each day?'

'You yourself explained why, sir,' I replied. 'We have to

make an example of them. We have to show the Barites how determined and serious we are. We can't tolerate further desertions.'

'One was hanged this morning,' said our leader. 'We could have hanged them all. We didn't do so. Why not?'

Dr Stre sat down on Sir John's bed, but the rest of us remained standing.

I replied:

'To quadruple the force of the example.'

Sir John said:

'Lieutenant Hansen has just questioned our right first, to pass a sentence of death, and second, to implement one.'

'Your choice of pronoun, sir,' said Hansen, 'seems to imply that you are including me, but I took no part in passing sentence.'

Well inside the tent, sitting at our leader's table, was his Indian scribe, probably engaged in copying out the entries of the previous evening from Sir John's diary.

'You were perfectly at liberty to express your views during our improvised trial,' said Sir John. 'You didn't do so. You were consequently a party to the sentence. *Qui tacet consentire videtur.*'

'Everything happened so quickly,' said Hansen, his gaze averted.

'Did I prevent you from speaking?' asked Sir John.

'What I came here to discuss,' said Hansen, his gaze still averted, 'was not our right to pass sentence. I came here to beg you not to carry out the three remaining executions. That was why I came here.' Then, tendering his apologies, he left the tent.

After a moment's silence, Stre said:

'I imagine, sir, that we have been summoned here because you want to hear our opinion? Or did you perhaps wish to stage for us an example of obstructiveness?'

'I want to hear your opinion, of course,' replied Sir John.

The doctor lit one of his cigars. He looked round for an ash-tray and then dropped the match on the canvas flooring. I have pointed out before that Stre, on the strength of his medical knowledge, was always trying to occupy a position apart among those of us who stood nearest to Sir John. According to our contracts he is a lieutenant exactly like the rest of us, and must be regarded as subordinate to me in my capacity of commander *en second*. He was the only one of us who was seated—he was in fact half lying on Sir John's bed. He was the only one of us who was smoking, and he had thrown his used match on the tent floor. In all these respects his behaviour was significant of his attitude.

He now spoke:

'You've previously pointed out on several occasions, Sir John, that what you expect of us is not advice or opinions but loyalty.'

'I'm confronted by a difficult choice,' replied our leader. 'It's therefore quite natural that I should want to discuss the situation with you.'

Stre rose and went up to Sir John's scribe.

'What's your opinion?' he asked. 'Have the three doomed men been sufficiently punished by the execution of the fourth?'

The scribe and interpreter answered:

'I have never killed anyone. I have no weapon, not even a knife. I do not know, effendim. But we need bearers.'

The doctor turned to us:

'I think,' he said, 'that these words are as wise as they are obscure.'

'I shouldn't willingly repeat an experience like that of this morning,' said Smitt. 'It wasn't a hanging, it was a bungled shooting.'

Smitt had just arrived at the boma with the rearguard, and had not yet had time to change his clothes. The right-hand pocket of his jacket had been torn loose, his trousers were dirty, and his wet clothes were glued to his body. He had lost more weight than any of us. The trouble he had had with sunburn had ceased after we entered the forest, but on this particular evening he was afflicted by several severe insect-bites round one eye.

Sir John turned to me.

'And you, Lieutenant Laronne?' he asked.

'I've a definite opinion,' I replied, 'but I shall refrain from expressing it. You can rely on my full support, whatever you decide to do, sir.'

During the whole of this discussion Sir John maintained the greatest calm. When I arrived at his tent he was leaning slightly against his table, and in this position he remained. He sometimes turned his head or the upper part of his body, but I cannot remember that he ever moved his feet. At last he said:

'However repugnant I may find it, I feel it is necessary to hang another of the deserters. This will be done early tomorrow morning as planned. Two deaths are required if the greater number of us is to survive.'

'Are you quite sure of this, sir?' asked Smitt.

'Yes,' answered Sir John. 'We shall reprieve the other two men who are sentenced to death.'

I went to see Hansen in his tent.

'You must understand,' I said. 'We've a task to perform and in order to accomplish it we must overcome all obstacles put in our way, all our internal and external difficulties. These difficulties create their own laws.'

Smitt was in the tent when I arrived. He had changed into dry clothes.

Hansen said:

'This is a relief expedition, Lieutenant Laronne, but it is growing more and more like a journey of discovery.'

Dr Stre too came to Hansen's tent. 'I heard voices,' he

said. 'Has the referendum been succeeded by a cabinet meeting?'

He went up to Smitt and examined his eye. 'I suspect that it's a bee-sting,' he said. 'Have you been looking for honey? It's very painful, isn't it? I'll give you some drops of belladonna and one of cocaine. That will ease the pain and tomorrow you'll be all right.'

We ate a very simple meal of cold tinned meat and bread. With this we emptied the last two remaining bottles presented by Niederselters.

The rain was pouring down in buckets. It was very cold, and our breath was visible at times.

It was impossible to light a fire. Said was ill, and Smitt made coffee for us in the dining-tent, over a paraffin flame that gave off black smoke and showered specks of greasy soot on the table and floor.

'There are times when one regrets the absence of the Portuguese's burning fifth zone,' said Dr Stre. 'We are now where it ought to be, but I am shivering like a dog.'

'They were mistaken about the earth's five zones,' said Sir John. 'The remarkable thing is that they clearly realized that it was a globe. Columbus, for example, was convinced to start with that the earth was spherical, but later on he came to the conclusion that it was pear-shaped. It is a fascinating idea.

'In actual fact,' he continued, 'it wasn't Columbus who discovered America. It was really a man called Rodrigo. It happened on the night between the eleventh and the twelfth of October, two hours and six minutes after midnight. Visibility was good and the moon was shining.'

'You've a very good memory, sir,' said Stre.

'Unfortunately not,' replied our leader, 'but there are certain things that have stuck, for instance, those two hours and six minutes after midnight.'

'Any other details?' asked Dr Stre. 'Any other details that have stuck fast in your memory?'

'Columbus gave Rodrigo a velvet doublet as a reward,' said Sir John. 'He was one of the crew of the *Santa Maria* and by some writers he is called Rodriguez. Later on the Catholic Queen Isabella gave him ten thousand maravedis in gratitude for his discovery.

'Maravedis?' asked Stre.

'The Spanish coin in use at that time,' answered our leader.

'And its value?'

'I fear I am unable to remember.'

'Approximately?'

'Rodrigo's financial reward was equal to a hundredth part of the total cost of Columbus' expedition. You may say that it cost a million maravedis to discover America.'

'And a velvet doublet,' added our doctor.

Sir John scraped out his pipe into one of the tins that had contained the meat for our evening meal.

'Have you ever reflected, Dr Stre,' he said, 'on what becomes obvious from the fact that Columbus sailed west? Or on what is equally obvious from the fact that Marco Polo's journeys were to the east? Or on what it was that made it natural for Henry the Infante to send his vessels south?'

'I'm sorry, sir,' answered Stre, 'but I don't know what you mean.'

'I'm alluding to the fact that the world has been discovered, and is still being discovered, from Europe by Europeans. One may say that discovery is a European occupation.'

'I'm afraid I haven't given the subject much thought.'

'I'm aware that I don't always express myself clearly.'

'If the truth must be told,' said our doctor, 'I wish I'd refrained from taking part in the discovery of this jungle.'

Jaffar Topan

We saw the remains of dead elephants.

'They have been killed by the pygmies,' said Uli.

'Those tiny men?'

'Yes, even these, the largest of all animals. One arrow is enough if it hits them in the right place. The hide of the elephant is covered with bark. You need an axe or a very strong knife when you cut up an elephant.'

The very cold rain fell all night. It was dark when we cleared a space for the boma, though the sun had not yet set. No fires could be lit and our camp was therefore small.

When I returned to my tent I had to shine my lamp on the ground ahead, not so that I might avoid prickly branches and sharp stumps—for like Sir John and his officers I wore shoes—but in order not to tread on the reclining or sitting men who were huddled together wherever leafy plants offered some shelter from the rain.

Uli said:

'There are folds of skin between the legs and the body where the flesh is practically unprotected, and where an arrow can penetrate. An elephant hit in the eye or the mouth dies quickly. An elephant has small eyes.'

Mali, our Bakva prisoner, said:

'They do not shoot from in front if they can help it. An arrow aimed from behind that hits them under the tail can also kill.'

Halmadi, the Syrt, said:

'I have never eaten the flesh of an elephant. There is a sura called The Elephant, but I remember nothing about it. The flesh must be allowed.'

Mali told us that the pygmies also caught elephants in pitfalls.

We could not believe him. Wouldn't a pitfall for an elephant have to be enormously big? And wasn't it difficult enough to dig a grave that would just hold a fallen Barite?

Mali and Uli laughed at our ignorance. An elephant pitfall need be no more than a shallow furrow, dug along one side of an elephant trail. Its only purpose was to cause the elephant to stumble and fall.

A goat can leap down from many times the height of a man. A monkey can fall from a tree-top. He weighs no more than a bunch of feathers, and he will bounce up in the best of health and vanish.

'An elephant need only fall,' said Uli. 'His own bulk will kill him as he falls. His lungs will be torn to shreds by the bones that surround them. His entrails will burst, his neck will be broken by the weight of his head.'

My tent was all too small in that cold rain. Said, the boy from Amman, slept furthest in. Kingiri sat close beside him with Halmadi by his side, both of them shivering with cold. By the opening of the tent were the copper-helmeted Uli and Mali, the Bakva prisoner.

I awoke to find the rain had stopped. My legs ached. The first fires were beginning to flare up, hesitantly, hissing with moisture, but warming nevertheless.

I filled my lamp with paraffin from our store.

Some of the Barites were roasting small, unripe manioc tubers over their fires. After they had been roasted they had to be mashed and rinsed in water to get rid of the bitter taste.

The three deserters sentenced to death lay huddled together under a thin shelter of fern-leaves. They were guarded by five Gallas. Two of the prisoners were asleep, the third was awake.

'I recognize you,' I said to the man who was awake. 'You are Kitete. It was you who wanted compensation because the Gallas had killed your slave Ali.'

'What do you want with me?' asked Kitete.

'Once you were well clothed,' I said. 'You wore a long-sleeved shirt. You had a green jacket. It is in rags now. You had a green fez. Where have you lost it? From what place do you come?'

He told me the name of a place I did not know. His face was gloomy, but he spoke calmly and in a low voice.

'I was one well clothed,' he said. 'I was a fisherman. Many fishes have hung in my net. I cultivated pepper and cloves. I was thrifty. I gave alms as we are instructed to do, but I could still afford to buy two slaves. One of them, Bandangi—I called him Ali—was shot by the Gallas. The other, Abdul, was hanged yesterday morning. And here am I. I find it hard to sleep.'

'To what place did you intend to flee?' I asked, and he replied:

'I awoke before daybreak. I was tired and hungry. I woke the two who lay nearest me and told them that we would go back, out of the forest. On Bari there are no forests. We each took a rifle. I woke my slave, Abdul, and gave him a rifle too.'

'Did you think you would get out of the forest alive?' I asked.

'On Bari there are no forests,' he answered. 'I was a

fisherman and cultivated spices. And here am I. I cannot sleep.'

Kitete dug into the moss and twigs with his bound feet until his toes found a dead snake. He lifted it towards me, and dropped it near my shoes.

'He fell upon me yesterday evening when we were settling down for the night. My hands are bound as well as my feet, but I killed him with a branch before he had time to strike.'

The snake was stiff and lifeless, but its skin was still soft and pliable, and had a moist gleam of barely discernible yellow, red, and green. Colours lose much of their brightness in the nocturnal light shed by a lamp and a faintly burning fire. Its fangs were large. There was not room for them in its mouth. They hung down on either side of its jaws.

'I did not let him strike though I shall be hanged in a few hours, or tomorrow, or the day after tomorrow,' said Kitete.

One of the Galla guards asked:

'What is he saying?'

I answered him in his own language:

'He says that he will give you the snake. It is not often that one becomes the owner of a snake killed by a man sentenced to death.'

I threw the snake to him and he caught it with his bundle of three spears.

'How old are you?' I asked Kitete.

'So old that I have already lived my life,' he answered. 'Why do you ask? Why do you not go away? I asked for compensation for my slave, Ali. I was told in reply that no man can own another man. Who owns me? Do I own myself? I was beaten with a switch, and they said that no one could own another. Yet someone must own me now.

'Why do you not go away?' he said. 'It is growing light.

I am no longer cold. I cannot leave this place. Surely I must belong to someone?'

Kitete's fellow prisoners were fast asleep. They were almost entirely naked, and very thin. Ants, beetles and grubs were crawling over them, and in their sleep they tried to defend themselves against the stings of these insects. I did not yet know the names of his fellow prisoners. One of them had an abscess as large as a fist under one ear.

Kitete asked me:

'If you had to draw one of three sticks, which would you draw?'

'If you yourself held out three sticks, two long and one short, would you put the short one in the middle, between the two long ones?'

He held out his hands tentatively.

'Think hard,' I said.

'The short one in the middle?'

'The two long ones on either side of the short one,' I said.

'No,' he said at last, 'not the short one in the middle. A long stick in the middle and the short one on one or other side of it.'

Dajatsj, the Galla captain, was sleeping outside the opening of my tent. He lay on his right side in a slight curve. The muzzle of his rifle peeped out behind the back of his neck. Even in sleep he kept a firm grip on his three short spears.

He had not troubled to raise even a simple shelter against the rain that had just ceased. His shirt, originally white, now torn and dirty, clung to his body. His face was hidden by the shield firmly fastened to his left arm. The long lion's mane on this shield lay like a thin veil around his waist.

I spread my mat over him. It was probably a meaningless gesture; it was beginning to grow light, or would soon begin to do so. We should all be awakened and begin a new day.

Moreover, I believed it was true that the Gallas could endure cold and wet better than the Barites could endure humidity and heat.

Kingiri, the six-fingered captain, woke when I opened the flap of the tent. His inflamed eyes blinked in the beam of my lamp. His face was scraggy and wrinkled. His mouth was dry, and he tried to moisten his lips with his tongue, and the tongue traced the length of his mouth up through his cheeks.

He reached for his pipe, but I took it.

'Not now, effem,' I said. 'It will soon be morning. Not now.'

He sat up. I put aside his hand.

'I know,' I said. 'You have never dwelt anywhere. But it will soon be morning. Not now, Kingiri, effem.'

I gave him water to drink.

'I should like to see these pygmies who can kill an elephant by making him fall,' he said.

He drank some of the water.

'And their poison,' he said. 'Must there not be a great deal of meat on an elephant?'

Laronne

I

The coffee we drank at breakfast had been made by Smitt over one of the Barite fires. He apologized for the fact that it was probably not as strong as it ought to be, but assured us that it was at least as hot as usual. I took his apologies on the subject of its strength with equanimity. I had never been able to resign myself to Sir John's partiality for thick black coffee, but we were certainly in need of a hot drink after the preceding night.

None of us commented upon the solid ingredients of this breakfast, which consisted of two biscuits and a piece of almost unchewable cassava-bread per person.

Dr Stre reported that Said, Sir John's servant, had been given one gramme of quinine in a little red wine the previous evening, and the same dose this morning, and that he would probably be quite well in a few days' time.

It proved to be impossible to find the rope—in actual fact a log-line—with which the first deserter had been hanged. Sjimba had taken charge of it, but it had been stolen during the night.

In spite of this, preparations for the execution were well in hand when the fall-in was sounded. A coarse rope, made of lianas, had been thrown over a suitable branch, and a piece of pliable rope, just long enough to form a loop, attached to its end.

Thirty of Halmadi's askaris had received orders to do the hauling. A rope of liana slips much less readily over a gnarled branch than a log-line.

Sir John made a short speech, in which he asked if one of the deserters was ready to be hanged voluntarily this morning.

None of them answered, and he held out the three sticks, one short and two long, to the Galla captain.

Dajatsj moved backwards.

'I am a soldier, sir,' he said, 'not a hangman.'

'You took the sticks and held them out yesterday.'

'I did not know what they meant,' he answered.

'You refuse?'

'I am only a soldier, sir,' answered Dajatsj, moving back another couple of steps.

In order that the proceedings should not be delayed our leader turned to his Indian scribe and interpreter, and gave him the sticks.

He laid them in his right hand so that the ends stuck out between his fingers.

'Now go,' said Sir John.

The scribe walked up to the three prisoners. He did not need to advance many steps. The boma we had cleared was very small and we were all standing close together.

He held out his hand with the three sticks. The prisoners hesitated and I heard him say:

'Draw now. The man who does not draw will get the stick that is left.'

One of them quickly drew the middle stick. The second man was longer in making his choice, and the short stick was left to the last man.

The ill-fated man's hands were bound behind his back. He had an abscess on his neck which was burst by the noose so that blood and water ran down over his naked chest.

He was asked if he had anything to say. His name was Omar and he came from the city of Bari.

Sir John's scribe and interpreter said:

'He says that the wound under his ear causes him pain. He says that he believes the pain will soon cease. He says that Allah is the Lord of the earth and of all mankind. He says that he is now going to take the shortest and easiest way out of this accursed forest.'

Sir John made a sign to the askaris' bugler. The doomed man was hauled up and was very soon dead.

II

We never found the rope—the log-line—with which Abdul had been hanged. Someone had stolen it—as we later discovered—and cut it up into small pieces and sold these as amulets to the superstitious Barites. This rope was made of tarred cotton.

III

In spite of the Ajantis' vigilance, and the advance guard's many feet, Hansen managed to tread on one of the poisoned skewers concealed in the ground. Up to this time we had felt protected from this danger by our thick-soled boots.

The skewer went right through the sole of his boot, his foot and the upper leather. It had been planted on one side of the path. It was long, and firmly anchored between the roots of trees. Hansen sank to his knees, and then fell sideways, in spite of the fact that his injured leg was held upright by the skewer.

According to what Hansen himself told us, Kami, the captain of No. 6 Company, pulled his foot free. He then took off his boot and sock, and made deep incisions in the two openings of the wound, let the blood flow, sucked out the wound and spat. Kami also helped him by giving an injection of sal volatile.

Hansen pulled the skewer out of the ground and kept it. It was three feet long, as sharp as an awl, and so hard that you could not break it between your hands.

Hansen could not walk and had to be carried. During the afternoon he lay limp and apathetic, and replied incoherently to any questions put to him. By the evening he was considerably better. The swelling had gone down, his pulse had returned to normal, and he only complained of acute pain.

On this day too we marched past several remains of elephants. A couple of times the advance guard had arrows shot at them, but we never reached any village where we could replenish our supplies of provisions. Nevertheless our men were able to provide themselves with a small number of half-ripe fruit from a fairly large plantation of plantains.

Sir John said:

'It may appear that this forest, this region, is rich in vegetation, stinging insects, hostile natives, and poison, but has nothing of value in it. This is not so.'

'We are listening,' said Dr Stre. 'We are all very interested.'

'I've made a tentative calculation,' said our leader, 'according to which there must be at least two hundred thousand elephants in the area. Each elephant has on him an average of up to fifty pounds of ivory. If round about one hundred elephants per week could be brought down by hunters engaged for the purpose, the world market could have an annual supply of ivory to the value of more than a quarter of a million pounds sterling. My calculations are based on the prices that prevailed for many years in Amsterdam and London. This state of affairs might continue for at least twenty-five years without any falling off worth mentioning. After that one would have to reckon with some reduction.'

'A reduction,' said Dr Stre. 'How great?'

'That would depend on the reproductive capacity of the elephants,' said Sir John. 'Opinions are somewhat divided on this point. None the less I am convinced that ivory totalling in value between eleven and thirteen million pounds sterling could be offered for sale before the last elephant is killed.'

He added:

'Even so, ivory is no more than an insignificant item among all the natural assets which are waiting here for people to exploit them.'

IV

On the morning of the following day Sir John let it be known that he did not covet any man's life, that the purpose of our expedition was to save life, and that he would therefore pardon the two remaining deserters under sentence of death.

Jaffar Topan

Mali, our Bakva prisoner, said:

'In time we shall reach villages where there is food. We have gone slowly.'

'How big is the forest?' asked Kingiri.

'The pygmies are everywhere,' said Mali. 'They live in the forest. They do not grow anything, and they have no animals. They get their living partly as hunters, but they would starve if there were not clearings where full-sized men live. It is there that they get the things they lack. They pay for them with ivory and poison.'

'Where does the forest end?' asked Kingiri.

'They also get what they need because they are small,' said Uli.

'Because they are small?'

'Yes.'

'By reason of their smallness? What is so special about their smallness?'

'They must have struck a bargain over it,' answered Uli. 'They have forgone their right to be full-grown. They must have been given something in exchange.'

'Where does this forest end?' asked Kingiri.

'Uli says that the pygmies must have received something in exchange for their smallness,' I said.

Intense heat followed the cold rain. The forest grew denser than ever before. Walking in it would have been like walking in the dark, if our eyes had not been given good time to get accustomed to it.

Said could walk, but he was too weak to carry anything. He was only a boy.

Halmadi, the woollen-mantled one, said:

'Truly those who have strayed shall eat of Al Zakkum, the tree of Hell. They shall fill their bellies with it, drink scalding water like feverish camels.

'This forest is made only of zakkum trees,' he continued. 'They bear no fruit, they do not even have flowers. They have only the uneatable heads of jinn's.'

We cleared a space for our camp that night on a low hill amidst tree-trunks like pillars. There was a pool of slimy, green water. A very thin layer of soil rested on very fine pale sand. Many of the Barites ate of this sand. They dug it out with their hands, dipped their tongues in it and swallowed without chewing.

Kingiri asked Uli:

'Where are your pygmies, your small, agile men?'

'All round us,' he answered. 'It is they who plant the poisoned skewers in the path ahead of us.'

'I have not yet seen any of them.'

'They have seen you,' answered Mali.

'Call to them.'

'Call?'

'Yes. Now.'

'Do you really wish it?' asked Uli.

'Am I not begging you to?'

Uli rose and went up to one of the two entrances to the boma. Mali went with him. They stopped near the Galla guards. Mali cupped his hands round his mouth, and called into the darkness. We waited.

'No one answers,' said Kingiri.

Mali called a second time and a third.

Upon that an arrow came from above and buried itself in the ground quite close to us. It did not fall by its own weight. It flew whining through the air, and drove deep into the ground with great force.

'The pygmies have answered,' said Uli.

I pulled out the arrow. It was as long as my arm. It was made entirely of wood, and tapered gradually to a point as sharp as a needle. The blunt end was cleft, and in the slit a dry leaf was held fast.

Notes on a Technique

by Per Olof Sundman

(Adapted from an article in *Bonniers Litterära Magasin*, March 1963)

Writing a book is the author's own affair, his pleasure and his pain. His part in it begins with the first letter that he sets down on paper, and ends with the last. What happens after that lies largely beyond his control. As a literary entity a book is essentially a product, or a series of products that emanate from the printed text and the individual reader.

Of course this statement is a truism, but I believe it bears repeating over and over again.

A good deal has been said and written about me as a novelist with a theory. One critic has even described me as the most obstinate of all obstinate novelists with theories. I must confess that I am somewhat perplexed by this. It would appear that many people believe that I have worked out a system, the rules of which I keep jotted down on a paper beside my typewriter, and that I adapt my ideas and correct my choice of words and expressions to accord with these rules, from which I could depart whenever I chose, but to which I glumly and obstinately adhere.

I do not think I hold anything so circumscribing as a

theory on novel-writing. In my case it is more a question of a very simple technique of story-telling, a simple sort of literary method.

The basic idea in my technique is this: I keep the story-telling within the bounds of external happenings. I never indulge in psychological reconstructions of what is going on inside my imagined characters. This restrictive approach is natural to me.

I am very fond of oral story-telling. I like making up stories about people I have met or events and incidents that I have experienced, but I never venture beyond the behaviour or actions of these people. This comes naturally to me. I see what they do, I hear what they say, I observe their facial expressions and the movements of their fingers, and I can reproduce these things in my stories. Beyond that I know nothing. Speculations about *inner developments*, feelings, intentions, and reasons can never be more than speculations. Moreover I fancy I have discovered that these *inner developments* are entirely unnecessary; they do not carry the story any further, and however well they are expressed they do not add one jot to its value.

In my short stories and my novels I have followed the same restrictive practice as in my oral story-telling. From a purely technical point of view the result has been that I almost always leave the telling of the story to one character, and allow him to describe the sequence of events to the reader. Ostensibly, I as author stand completely aside. I endeavour to limit my story-teller's narrative to what I imagine he would have described if he had been a living person. For instance, if I myself am telling a story orally, I cannot give an account of everything that may have happened. I impose restrictions on myself. I carry out a far-reaching process of deletion, while at the same time I emphasize the importance of certain details of the story.

This is how it acquires shape and form and is also the means whereby I give the hearer a portrait of myself.

The same thing happens in the case of my imaginary story-teller. He must describe an event or a fellow human being and his story must be both selective and emphatic. I must also be conscious that he is giving a portrait of himself by underlining certain details and circumstances, and by failing to notice or partially or completely ignoring others. This method has had a great influence on the content of my novels, though what is actually said may seem to be of little interest.

I am deeply interested in the relationship of the individual to the people about him, in the position he occupies in a group, large or small, and in the attitude he adopts as a member of a community. I am a realist, you see.

The community in which we live, well developed as it is technically and economically, has many positive advantages. It gives us more freedom, inasmuch as we have more time at our disposal, and greater opportunities for showing personal preferences. It gives us safety and security, but it also has disadvantages.

Prosperity is a complicated mechanism; it is sensitive to interference; it presupposes order and discipline. Welfare demands flexibility and adaptability from the individual. This results in a tendency towards diminished personal liberty which, in my view, must be watched with the utmost vigilance.

This tendency is easier to observe and describe in small communities, in thinly populated areas like the commune in which I live. I could give many examples, from expropriation by companies developing electric power to the politics of the State's housing policy, from the activities of those responsible for the social services to the building and upkeep of private drives.

A number of years ago I committed an offence against

personal liberty. I took the initiative in depriving a man of his freedom for at least three months.

This step necessitated suffering. That the loss of liberty would cause him distress goes without saying. There was also good reason to suppose that it would inflict permanent injury. All the same it was a step that had to be taken for the sake of the man's family. Moreover it was sanctioned by our civic laws.

This was the episode that prompted me to write *The Investigation* (*Undersökningen*), a novel about a day in the life of the chairman of a rural council committee for the prevention of drunkenness.

My original intention was to illustrate the impossibility of discovering what lies beneath a fellow human being's exterior; the necessity that we should admit this limitation, and replace unattainable knowledge by tolerance, far-sightedness and understanding, not only as individuals, but also as the representatives of local authorities.

The events described are seen through the eyes of a fairly young, but trusted local official, by occupation a tallyman in a timber-yard, composed and sceptical, both when putting a question and when making a comment. Not particularly well-read, if you except proclamations and regulations. He has many responsibilities. He knows his own commune and carries all the cares of the district about with him in his brief-case.

What he has to tell, what he notices and what he reports have all to bear the imprint of his office. Consequently my novel about the need for tolerance, and the impossibility of obtaining definitive information about another human being, expanded automatically into the story of a district and the conditions of life prevailing in it.

The events described in *The Investigation* are imaginary. The circumstances which brought them about, i.e. the laws governing drunkenness and their application, are nevertheless realities, they belong to the world of everyday experience. The matter I wanted to discuss, our lack of tolerance and our failure to realize that there is a limit to what we can know, I also regard as a reality.

I felt I had to make my novel produce the illusion that I was describing a *real* event. Otherwise I should run the risk of seeming to be tilting at windmills.

I made use of the old, well-known trick. I filled out the main theme of the story with a series of *true* details, of no importance in themselves, such as information about wind and weather, the tallyman's conditions of work, the carrying capacity of the buses, what happens when dynamite is detonated, the surface of the floor of a living-room and also, of course, a great many scraps of information about the chief character in his role as the representative of his council. These numerous pieces of information about details can be accepted without question. They are slightly tedious and boring, they appear to be unimportant. In a word they are credible; they overflow with credibility and confer upon the imaginary events an air of indisputable truth.

I succeeded so well that the majority of the critics described *The Investigation* as a form of literary reporting, the description of an actual event.

But I was caught out by my own method. I discovered that these supposedly unrelated details were not in themselves unrelated. They proved to have a value of their own; they seemed to increase the possibility of describing and discussing the situation of a man among other men. Thereupon I wrote *The Shot* (Skytten), a story concerned with details.

The Expedition has been variously understood by the critics as a pastiche in the style of Stanley, as a description of the idea behind all travel, as a symbolic representation of the history of mankind, as a discussion of the problems of living in a community, even as a plea for an authoritarian form of government. This is as it should be. A novel cannot be unambiguous like a text-book of the four simple operations of arithmetic. It must be open to various interpretations and these will depend on the make-up of the interpreter. It has been said that I entertain *a predilection* for the strong, capable man and that I admire such men. It is not so much a question of admiration and predilection as of *interest*, and this interest is connected with the part the strong man plays in our society, and the great importance he has for the rest of us.

Stanley has long fascinated me. A traveller and a conqueror who attacked and overcame all obstacles, a brutal colonizer who appears never for a moment to have doubted the birthright of the white gentleman. The expedition for the relief of Emin Pasha stands out as the most remarkable of all his undertakings; this journey that lasted two and a half years, that cost twenty-seven thousand seven hundred and nine pounds, nine shillings and five pence, seven or nine hundred human lives, and an incalculable amount of suffering.

The portrait we have of Stanley is in the main a facsimile of the portrait he drew of himself in his books. For instance, the greater part of what we know of the Emin Pasha expedition comes from Stanley's own account. I felt I wanted to describe and investigate the type of human being personified by Stanley from another angle.

Stanley drew boundary lines not only between white men and coloured men, but also between the various classes of white men. Consequently one of the Europeans who took part in the Emin Pasha expedition is not once mentioned by name in Stanley's bulky book, although they were close companions every day, possibly every hour. This man's name was Hoffman, and he was not a gentleman. He was Stanley's servant. On the few occasions when we are made aware of his existence his master is making fun of him, as for instance when he showed surprise at finding that the water of the Red Sea was not red.

Our knowledge of the strong man and his expedition would be wider if we also had a description of events by Hoffman, among others, not because it would be *truer*, but because it would be different.

I made an attempt to let a servant of the Hoffman type tell us about a leader of an expedition who resembled Stanley. The attempt was a failure. He turned out to be such a poor hand at telling a story that no publisher would have accepted his manuscript.

Then I turned the story-telling over to Jaffar Topan (I do not know how his name should be pronounced), a non-European of doubtful origin, a gifted linguist and a man who could both write and count.

As the work progressed the emphasis shifted from Sir John, the leader of the expedition, to the expedition itself, to the way in which it was organized and the unifying and disruptive forces at work among groups and individuals.

A need developed for information that Jaffar was unable to supply, simply because he was the man he was. I found myself forced to introduce another narrator, the European lieutenant, Laronne. And I was back again with my main preoccupation, the position of the individual in a group.

Some critics have complained that in *The Expedition* I have abandoned my *literary* method. I cannot share this view.

I have still used the simple technique which comes naturally to me. I am mainly concerned with *externals*. The story is told from the point of view of one person, and I restrict what he notices and remarks upon to what I imagine he would have told us about if he had been a living person and my imaginary sequence of events had been real happenings.

The fact that I have used two narrators makes no essential difference.

I have also tried, with the help of many little *true* details, to create the illusion that it is a story of real events. In my previous books I was able to gather these details from the reality in which I spent my days. In *The Expedition* I had to seek for them in my bookcase, and that not without both pleasure and toil. The one method of approach is as practical as the other.

Two critics, in particular, perplexed me. They appeared to regard Sir John, the leader of the expedition, as a mouthpiece for my personal views. They seemed to believe that I approve of his demand for absolute loyalty, that I personally am in sympathy with his spartan social code.

It is possible that they have been led astray by my literary technique. Of the two narrators it is Laronne, the tough second-in-command, who furnishes us with the most straightforward description of Sir John as the leader and organizer. But Laronne is an imaginary narrator, he does not represent the author. He is a fictional, subjective story-teller; his account does not contain any fictional objective truth. And the imaginary character Laronne and the real Sundman have very little in common.